Dear M

Perhaps you will
enjoy these informal
essays on the veins of
my very favorite
scientist on matters
of science and
general human
interest, including
taverns!! Happy
years! Sincerely
1/8/59 Donald C. Slutcher

SCIENCE IN A TAVERN

Essays and Diversions on Science in the Making

Science in a Tavern

ESSAYS AND DIVERSIONS
ON SCIENCE IN THE MAKING

CHARLES S. SLICHTER

1958

MADISON

THE UNIVERSITY OF WISCONSIN PRESS

Published by the University of Wisconsin Press
430 Sterling Court, Madison 6, Wisconsin

Copyright © 1938 and 1940 by the University of Wisconsin
Second edition, second printing, 1958

Lithography by Cushing-Malloy, Inc., Ann Arbor, Michigan
Printed in the United States of America

Library of Congress Catalog Card Number 40–31088

Publisher's Note

FIVE of these essays were first presented as addresses before the Madison Literary Club: "The Royal Philosophers," "The Club," and "The Side Shows of Science," hitherto unpublished, on April 10, 1922, October 8, 1928, and January 9, 1939, respectively; "Industrialism" on June 12, 1911, and "Polymaths: Technicians, Specialists, and Genius" on June 13, 1932. The last two were subsequently published, the one in the *Popular Science Monthly* for October, 1912, and the other in the *Sigma Xi Quarterly* for September, 1933.

"The Principia and the Modern Age" was read on September 7, 1937, before the Mathematical Association of America at State College, Pennsylvania, at a meeting commemorating the two hundred and fiftieth anniversary of the publication of Newton's *Principia* and was thereafter published in the *American Mathematical Monthly* for August-September, 1937.

The annual meeting of the Central Association of Science and Mathematics Teachers in Chicago on December 2, 1933, was the occasion on which Dean Slichter presented "Science and Reality." "Science and Authority" was delivered at the initiation banquet of Alpha chapter of Alpha Chi Sigma, on December 8, 1934. Both these addresses were later published—the

PUBLISHER'S NOTE

first, under a slightly different title, in *School Science and Mathematics* for March, 1934, and the other in the *Hexagon* for January, 1935.

"The New Philosophy" and "Heaven's Highway" were read before the University of Wisconsin chapter of Phi Beta Kappa, the one in May, 1921, and the other in May, 1936. "The Self-Training of a Teacher," delivered before the mathematics session of the Summer School for Engineering Teachers at the University of Minnesota on September 5, 1931, was published in the October, 1931, issue of the *Journal of Engineering Education*.

The courtesy of the publishers who have granted permission to reprint these essays is gratefully acknowledged.

Preface

IT WAS with much pleasure that I received the request of the University Press to publish these writings. The essays are, of course, a by-product in the life of a busy teacher. Perhaps they have some value because they contain hidden within them a little of the unwritten and unwritable history of the forced growth of an American university. I myself cannot point out that concealed story, but I have no doubt it exists. I recognize that I am not the only person who began life on the staff of an American institution when its students numbered about three hundred and served for half a century until the attendance rose to ten thousand or more, but the experience is at least unique in the sense that it cannot happen again. No one could have lived a happier life. It was life in an expanding universe, with the duties thrust upon me always just beyond my powers. I have learned that it is striving after things we cannot quite accomplish that leads to contentment.

Perhaps I should apologize for the historical material that appears in some of the essays. I am no expert, and gossip and romance may sometimes have appealed to me more than fact. The essay on the Royal Philosophers is based on the history of the club issued to members only and edited by Professor Geikie. My copy was presented to me by a member—I believe there are only two or three copies in America. The account of The Club is also based on a volume issued to members only. The only copy I have been able to find in this country is in the Congressional Library at Washington.

I dedicate this little volume to the four sons of Mary Louise Slichter; it is these five who, with my former students, have educated me from a crude beginning to a most happy maturity.

CHARLES S. SLICHTER

Madison, Wisconsin
September, 1938

Contents

SCIENCE IN A TAVERN

I live in the crowd of jollity, not so much to enjoy company as to shun myself.—DR. JOHNSON

Everyone wished to belong to some club or "college"; it provided the comforting sense of belonging to an exclusive society, a sense so dear to the hearts of gregarious men.—WALLACE FERGUSON

The Royal Philosophers

NOT all the heavy eaters and hard drinkers of past centuries have been poets and dramatists, or literary fellows. I propose to show that the men who led scientific progress in England during the seventeenth and eighteenth centuries were men who could and did eat and drink with almost as much gusto as did Shakespeare, Ben Jonson, Marlowe, Donne, Dekker, Dr. Johnson, Boswell, and other luminaries of literature and the arts. My story is about a dining club of scientific men that has been meeting in England for two or three centuries. This group is officially known as the Royal Society Club, but generally and unofficially as the Royal Philosophers.

The exact date when the club was formed is more or less uncertain. Its written minutes date only from 1743, but we know that for a generation or two before this its members had been dining together with regularity, and that at least one set of minutes has been lost. Everything indicates, in fact, that the club was merely the more or less formal continuation of a group of diners that since 1645 had been getting together on Thursdays, either at the Bull-Head Inn or at the residence of Dr. Goddard, to discuss the new or experimental philosophy. It was this group of diners, called by Boyle the "Invisible College," that in 1660 organized the "Visible College," which two years later was chartered as the Royal Society of London for the Improvement of Natural Knowledge. Prominent in the group were Lord Brouncker, a generous and enthusiastic patron of all branches of the new learning, although a specialist in none; Bishop Wilkins, master of Trinity College, best known for his eloquent exposition of the Copernican theory; Robert Boyle, the physicist and author of the *Defence of Christianity;* Sir William Petty, the political economist and statistician, whose side occupations were those of professor of anatomy at Oxford and professor of music at Gresham College; Christopher Wren, Savilian professor of astronomy at Oxford and later professor of astronomy at Gresham College, whose side lines were the planning of the military defenses of London and the building of St. Paul's Cathedral. This group, with about an equal number of less well known but equally enthusiastic associates, nearly all under thirty-five years of age, confirmed one of the great events in British history, when on July 15, 1662, they received the charter of the Royal Society from the king. On that foundation has been built the structure of British science. The men who constituted these first groups of organized science were not long-faced specialists nor academicians in the continental sense; they were convivial Englishmen, men chosen from all walks of life. In the early membership lists appear the names of a notable band of medical men, several members of parliament, amiable and versatile politicians, critics, civil servants, and pamphleteers. Among them were bishops like Samuel Squire, and explorers and travelers like Captain Middleton, an adventurer of the Hudson's Bay Company, and antiquarians like Martin Folkes, and all-round good fellows like Daniel Wray and Jeremiah Dyson, both of whom have been accused of writing the Junius letters.

To visualize the picture I am sketching for you, think first of a group of Englishmen from many different walks of life meeting about 1650, every Thursday afternoon, at the Bull-Head Tavern in Cheapside to eat and to experiment and to talk science. Think next of their success in organizing the Royal Society in 1662; think next of the formal meetings of the Royal Society every Thursday evening at Gresham College; think of a smaller group of enthusiasts— say from twelve to twenty—meeting for dinner Thursdays, first at three o'clock, later at four, at a London inn, afterward appearing at the Gresham College meeting full of wine and song; think of this smaller group of choice spirits as an informal continuation of the group that organized the Royal Society; finally, perhaps about 1725, becoming a dining club with regular meetings, a presiding officer and a treasurer, and a few informal rules and regulations.

The first treasurer of the Royal Philosophers was, on the authority of Sir Joseph Ayloffe, Dr. Halley the astronomer. The record covering his term of office has been lost. The extant records, as we have said, begin with 1743, when an apothecary and antiquarian named Josiah Colebrooke succeeded Halley as treasurer and keeper of the records. Colebrooke's accounts of the weekly meetings extend unbroken over a period of more than thirty years, and chronicle what is probably the most interesting period in the life of the club. Most of his entries are brief, but usually they give the names of those present and the fare served at the dinner, together with the resolutions and motions having to do with routine business. Others have given us in contemporary writings a hint of the customary activities of the club. Samuel Pepys records in his diary several meetings of the Royal Society that he attended between the years 1660 and 1669, and in nearly every instance mentions the dinner of the smaller group, which he also attended; for example, in 1668, after attending a meeting and contributing forty pounds toward the building of a college as the future home of the Society, Pepys states that "thence with Lord Brouncker and several of them to the King's Head Taverne by Chauncey Lane, and there did drink and eat and talk and, above the rest, I did hear of Mr. Hooke and my Lord [Brouncker] an account of the reason of concords and discords in musique, which they say is from the equality of vibrations."

But perhaps the best picture of one of the meetings of this convivial club of the Royal Society can be had from a scurrilous caricature printed anonymously at the beginning of the eighteenth century. The author was later ascertained to be one Ned Ward, a notorious wag and tavernkeeper of his day. He says:

"This eminent Club was at first establish'd by some of the principal Members of the *Royal Society,* and held every Thursday at a certain Tavern in Cornhill.

"The chief Design of the aforementioned Club was to propagate new Whims, advance mechanic Exercises, and to promote useless as well as useful Experiments. . . . No sooner were the patch'd Assembly met together on their Club-Night, but every Man, in hopes to advance his Reputation would be so wonderfully busy about one Experiment or other, that the very Elements could not rest for 'em; And the whole Company divide themselves into so many several Cabals, that they sat like Train-Band-Men at a Captain's Treat, where there are four or six appointed to a Bottle. Some by those hermetical Bellows, called an Aeolipile, would be trying with an empty Bottle whether Nature would admit of a *Vacuum*. Others, like busy Chandlers, would be handling their Scales to nicely discover the Difference in the Weight between Wine and Water."

ſ

JOSIAH COLEBROOKE, the second treasurer of the Royal Philosophers, was a remarkable character, who served the club, as has been said, for more than thirty years, attending the fifty-two or fifty-three meetings a year with utmost regularity and describing its proceedings in quaint and frank language and with a fascinating naïvete. He was an accomplished diner-out and conversationalist, having a firm conviction that for his countrymen strong meat and stronger drink were indispensable. Nothing savoring of French cookery appears in the menus during his term of office. There were few soups or made dishes. His bill of fare usually began with two kinds of fish, followed by several joints, such as boiled leg of pork, roast beef, leg of mutton, roast turkey, and boiled fowls, with a pudding of some kind, and an apple pie or tart, and butter and cheese to conclude the repast. So much was he attached to plum pudding that almost every dinner had at least one, and sometimes two or three, of this English concoction; of the fifty-two weekly dinners during the year, there were generally over forty at which the national dish was served.

For nearly forty years the weekly dinners were held at the "Mitre Tavern in Fleet Street over against Fetter Lane." When in 1780 the Royal Society moved to Somerset House, the dinners were held at the Crown and Anchor Tavern in the Strand, where they continued to be given for sixty-eight years.

The annals of the Royal Society do not include Colebrooke's minutes in full, but short extracts are given, from which I can give a few sample menus. Here is the earliest one, that for March 24, 1747:

> *Two dishes fresh Salmon—Lobster sauce*
> *Cod's head*   *Fillet of Veal*
> *Pidgeon Pye*   *Chine of Pork*
> *Calves' Head*   *Plum Pudding*
> *Bacon and Greens*   *Apple Custard*
>   *Butter and Cheese*

The diners may have gone away hungry from this meeting, for later a "two-course" dinner is described:

Veale Soup   *Haunch of Venison*
Fresh Salmon and Smelts   *Soup and Bouille*
Two dishes of Chickens   *Cod and Smelts*
Boiled Turkey and Oyesters   *Aladobe*
Lamb pye with Cockscombs   *Ham*
Rump of Beef

RIDERS

Two dishes fruit   *Two Jellies and Syllabubs*
Two Almond Leach and Olives

SECOND COURSE

Two dishes Teale and Larks   *Tansie*
Pear Pye, Creamed   *Marrow Pudding*
Hare   *Two dishes Asparagus and Loaves*

In a note at the end Colebrooke says: "The company was this day entertained with the above dinner at 5/ per head eating and drank to the prosperity of the society in claret."

One might infer from Colebrooke's account that the poor diners had little to drink, for he rarely mentions liquor except as he records an exceptional toast. He takes the order of drinks as a matter of course, which it is unnecessary to record. But a visiting Frenchman has preserved for us an account that emphasizes the liquid portion of the dinners. It is true that his account is dated 1784, at a time when vegetables and other articles of food from the Continent had made an impression on old-fashioned British cooking. For after the Peace of Paris in 1763 the

9

stream of foreign visitors was again set in motion, and along with the numerous foreign guests entertained by the Royal Philosophers came changes in the menu and a gradual change in the dinner hour. In 1650 the dinner hour had been three o'clock; by 1780 it was four o'clock; and by 1784 it seems to have been moved ahead to four-thirty. Here is the amusing account given by the French visitor, one Faujas de St. Fond:

"We sat down to table about five o'clock. Sir Joseph Banks presided, and filled the place of honour. No napkins were laid before us; indeed there were none used; the dinner was truly in the English style.

"A member of the Club, who is a clergyman (I believe it was the astronomer Maskelyne), made a short prayer, and blessed the company and the food. The dishes were of the solid kind, such as roast beef, boiled beef and mutton prepared in various ways, with abundance of potatoes and other vegetables, which each person seasoned as he pleased with the different sauces which were placed on the table in bottles of various shapes.

"The beef-steaks and the roast beef were at first drenched with copious bumpers of strong beer, called porter, drunk out of cylindrical pewter pots which are much preferred to glasses because one can swallow a whole pint at a draught.

"This prelude being finished, the cloth was removed, and a handsome and well-polished table was covered, as if it were by magic, with a number of fine crystal decanters filled with the best port, madeira and claret; this last is the wine of Bourdeaux. Several glasses, as brilliant in lustre as fine in shape, were distributed to each person, and the libations began on a grand scale, in the midst of different kinds of cheese which, rolling in mahogany boxes from one end of the table to the other, provoked the thirst of the drinkers.

"To give more liveliness to the scene, the President proposed the health of the Prince of Wales: this was his birthday. We then drank to the Elector Palatine, who was that day to be admitted into the Royal Society. The same compliment was next paid to us foreigners of whom there were five present.

"The members of the Club afterwards saluted each other, one by one, with a glass of wine. According to this custom, one must drink as many times as there are guests, for it would be thought a want of politeness in England to drink to the health of more persons than one at a time.

"A few bottles of champagne completed the enlivenment of every one. Tea came next, together with bread and butter, and all the usual accompaniments: Coffee followed, humbly yielding preference to the tea, though it be the better of the two. In France we commonly drink only one cup of good coffee after dinner; in England they drink five or six of the most detestable kind.

"Brandy, rum, and some other strong liqueurs, closed this philosophic banquet which terminated at half-past seven, as we had to be at a meeting of the Royal Society summoned for eight o'clock. Before we left, however, the names of all the guests were written on a large sheet of paper and each of us paid six shillings: this was not dear.

"I repaired to the Society along with Mssrs. Banks, Cavendish, Maskelyne, Aubert, and Sir Henry Englefield; we were all pretty much enlivened, but our gaiety was decorous."

Now this sort of a night seems all right for robust men of the world, like Sir Joseph Banks and Captain James Cook. But it also had its appeal for delicate and dried-up scientists like Henry Cavendish, whose father, Lord Charles Cavendish, was a member of the club when he was proposed for membership at the age of twenty-seven. The biographer of Cavendish represents him as possessed of a singular love of solitude and of a reluctance to meet with his fellows. Yet this same Cavendish attended the meetings of his boisterous club with great regularity for fifty-two years. From 1770 to the end of his life, forty years later, his record was never less than forty-four attendances in the year, and usually fifty. In the year 1784, which began on a Thursday, there were fifty-three Thursdays; Cavendish was present at every meeting. After fifty-three meetings of this sort it is not difficult to appreciate his love of solitude.

The Royal Philosophers was an exclusive club. Membership was open to only a few, and only a few might be received as guests. Yet in the eighteenth century there was one easy way of breaking into it. At a special meeting on May 3, 1750—the president in the chair and fourteen members present—it was resolved: "That any Nobleman or Gentleman complimenting this company annually with venison, not less than a Haunch, shall during the continuance of such annuity be deemed an Honorary Member and admitted as often as he comes, without paying the fine which those members do who are elected by Ballott."

Now it is obvious that this resolution was quite unfair to anyone who might be in a position to furnish a Sea Turtle, and so on October 4, 1750, "Andrew Mitchell Esq. (a visitor then present) proposing to compliment the company with a Turtle which he expects very soon from the West Indies: It was resolved *nem. con.* that any Gentleman giving a Turtle annually should be considered an Honorary Member during the payment of that Annuity." It must be obvious, too, that these two resolutions put at a serious disadvantage those who were in a position to compliment the club only with domesticated products, and so we are glad to read from the dinner register that to correct this obvious injustice "William Hanbury Esq. having this day entertained the company with a Chine of Beef which was 34 inches in length and weighed upward of 140 lb., it was agreed *nem. con.* that two such Chines were equal to half a Buck or a Turtle, and entituled the donor to be an Honorary Member of this Society." In modern times the newspapers would probably refer to this as the "honorary membership graft."

We should not conclude the present topic, however, without noting a sad obituary; for the honest Colebrooke records in his minutes that "Andrew

Mitchell's, Esq., Turtle happening to die as the ship came up the Channel, the company dined" as follows:

Turkey Boiled and Oyesters	*Two dishes Herring*
Calves' Head, Hashed	*Tongue and Udder*
Fowles and Bacon	*Leg of Pork and Pease*
Chine of Mutton	*Sir Loin of Beef*
Apple Pye	*Plum Pudding*

Butter and Cheese

The membership of the club was limited to forty. Usually twelve to twenty attended the weekly dinners. Besides the honorary members who had earned their way, there was an interesting stream of foreign invited guests and of special British guests, who were evidently being tried out as possible timber for the Royal Society. Much could be written about the foreign celebrities who were entertained, for they included such names as Clairaut the French geometer, Stanislaus Augustus the scientist and the last king of Poland, Claude Adrian Helvetius, Volta, Lunardi, Cassini, Legendre, Cuvier, Berzelius, and Canova.

Of greatest interest to us, of course, are the American guests. The most prominent of these were our two Benjamins—Benjamin Franklin and Benjamin Thompson. The engaging personality of Benjamin Franklin was nowhere better revealed than in his British relations. In 1753 he received the Copley Medal of the Royal Society, and in 1756 he was unanimously elected a Fellow, without any knowledge on his part of the proposed honor. Now his election as Fellow was a remarkable event, for it constitutes the one exception to the Royal Society's policy of admitting new members only upon the request of an applicant vouched for by three members. Moreover, by another act of the Council, Franklin was relieved of the payment of all dues—which in those days were five guineas annually. In presenting the Copley Medal to Franklin's friend, Peter Collinson, to be transmitted by him to America, the president, Lord Macclesfield, said:

"This mark of distinction is doubly due Mr. Franklin. It is due to him as a philosopher, it is due to him as a man. The successful experiments of this philosopher have given us probable hopes of being one day able to secure ourselves from the dreadful effects of lightning. And the public spirit, the modesty, the goodness and benevolence of the man have been long conspicuous, and the effects of them long felt in the country where he resides."

On his first mission Franklin was in England five years, from 1757 to 1763. He landed on July 27, 1757; within two weeks the Royal Philosophers had him as their dinner guest, as they did frequently thereafter. During his second mission he was present at many of the meetings held during the ten-year interval 1764–74, usually as the guest of his close friend, Sir John Pringle. He attended as many as eighteen dinners in a single year.

An interesting meeting was the one held during the latter part of 1772 when Franklin and Boswell, of Johnsonian fame, were both present. Even more interesting must have been the meeting of December

10, 1773, when Joseph Priestly, Franklin, Pringle, and Boswell were all present as the guests of Sir John. Franklin's last meeting, in 1774, was also the last dinner provided by Josiah Colebrooke, after thirty-one years of service as treasurer. On this occasion you can think of our Benjamin eating heartily of the following menu:

Haddock	Shote and Soles
Stoved Eels	Boiled Beef
Two plumb puddings	Greens and Collyflower
Beans and Bacon	Venison Pastry
Knuckle of Veal	Forequarter of Lamb
Two Ducks	Two dishes pease
Two Cherry Tarts	Butter and Cheese

The other prominent American guest of the Royal Diners was Benjamin Thompson, born in 1753 in Massachusetts. This remarkable Benjamin was a Tory, and he was glad to get to England in 1776. There he took office and later returned to fight against his native land, arriving only in time for the final surrender, however. He then took service under the Elector Maximilian of Bavaria, who later made him Count Rumford, the name coming from the home town of his wife in New Hampshire. Rumford was a frequent guest at the dining club. When he became wealthy he founded the Rumford Medal of the Royal Society, the Rumford Medal of the American Society of Arts, and the Rumford Professorship at Harvard. His greatest contribution to society, however, was the founding in 1799, in conjunction with Joseph Banks, of the Royal Institution of Great Britain. He himself selected Sir Humphrey Davy as the first scientific lecturer for the Royal Institution.

An almost forgotten fact in scientific history is that the invention of the gas balloon in 1784 caused far more excitement throughout the world than did the invention of the aeroplane more than a century later. On September 15, 1784, Vincent Lunardi, then a young man of twenty-five, made a successful ascent in a gas-filled balloon from the artillery grounds, Moorfields, and descended near Ware in Hertfordshire—a distance of perhaps twenty-five miles. It was exactly a fortnight later that he dined with the Royal Philosophers. Lunardi's success created a fury of enthusiasm throughout the British Isles. He was feted and courted by the populace and received by the king. Balloons were the sole topic of conversation. Wigs, coats, hats, bonnets, neck scarfs were named "Lunardi" after the Italian aeronaut. At the end of the year Horace Walpole, recording the matter in his private memoirs, had this to say of the state of public excitement in London:

"This enormous Capital that must have some occupation, is most innocently amused with those philosophical playthings, air-balloons. But, as half a million people that impassion themselves for any object are always more childish than children, the good souls of London are much fonder of the *airgonauts* than of the toys themselves. Lunardi, the Neopolitan Secretary, is said to have bought three or four thousand pounds in the stocks by exhibiting his person, his balloon, and his dog and cat in the 'Pantheon,' for a shilling each visitor."

Even Quakers like Thomas Young were able to stand the gaiety of the Royal Philosophers. Young was a singularly gifted person. At the age of fourteen (1787) he had mastered Latin, Greek, French, Italian, Hebrew, Persian, and Arabic. At nineteen he had begun the study of medicine in London. A remarkable paper on the crystalline lens of the eye secured for him admission to the Royal Society at the unprecedented age of twenty-one. He then studied medicine at Edinburgh for a year, and for two years at Göttingen, where he took a degree. He spent two years at Cambridge, where he took another M.D. degree, and presently started the practice of medicine in London, which he continued there until his untimely death in 1829. In 1801 he was appointed professor of physics in the Royal Institution, where he gave ninety-one lectures in the two years of his professorship, lectures that in content were a whole generation ahead of his time. Young served on all sorts of commissions and secretariats, wrote continually on optical, medical, and other topics, and all the time maintained an active practice; he was the busiest medical man in London. This is the man who uncovered the secrets of hieroglyphics from the Rosetta Stone and applied the results to numerous other inscriptions. He was the first Egyptologist.

Young lived down many of his Quaker traditions. He was a frequent guest of the Royal Philosophers and eventually became a member of the noisy group.

He was quite un-Quakerlike in his interest in dress. Not only was he extraordinarily spruce and modish in his own dress, but, as the discoverer of some of the grandest and most occult laws of the spectrum, he could loiter with the ladies in a fashionable shop in Bond Street and help them in the choice of ribbons and millinery—applied optics, we might call it! Helmholtz has said of him that "he had the misfortune to be too greatly superior in sagacity to his contemporaries. They gazed at him with astonishment, but they could not always follow the bold flights of his intellect, and thus a multitude of his most important ideas lay buried and forgotten in the great tomes of the Royal Society, until a later generation re-made his discoveries and convinced itself of the accuracy and force of his inferences."

If we could have dined with the Royal Philosophers through all the generations since 1650, we would have met, either as members or as visitors, most of the distinguished scientists of Great Britain. There would have been one notable exception, however—we would never have supped with Isaac Newton.

Newton became a Fellow of the Royal Society in 1672. He was made warden of the mint in 1694, and three years later master of the mint. This last office required him, soon after his appointment, to move to London, where he was a regular attendant at the Royal Society. In 1702 he became its president, but this office did not then carry with it ex-officio membership in the Royal Philosophers, as it did after they were formally organized many years later. There

19

is no evidence that Newton ever enjoyed the convivial dinner company of his friends Halley, Wren, Hooke, Pepys, and others of the exclusive set.

ℐ

I DO NOT know that there is such a thing as a genealogy of tavern clubs. But there was an Age of Taverns, just as now there is an Age of Social Clubs, and of Elks, Moose, Beavers, Eagles, Blackhawks, et cetera. Ben Jonson and Shakespeare and their pals meeting at the Mermaid, and Ben Jonson, Dekker, and others meeting as the Apollo Club at the Devil Tavern, were, in a sense, of the same genealogical line as the scientific group meeting at the Bull-Head in 1650 and at the Mitre in 1750. It is therefore interesting to speculate whether the organization of The Club by Joshua Reynolds in 1764 was not suggested by the success of the Royal Philosophers. Reynolds must have known of the existence of the Philosophers before The Club was founded, for he had been admitted as a Fellow of the Royal Society in 1761. There is no evidence, however, that he had been a guest of the Royal Philosophers before 1790.

It appears, too, that Dr. Johnson was never a guest of the scientific diners, notorious lover of taverns though he was. In a confessional mood he once said that "there is no private house in which people can enjoy themselves so well as at a capital tavern," and there is "nothing which has yet been contrived by man by which so much happiness is produced as by a good tavern or inn." A man who held these views and who haunted the inns as Johnson did must have known a good deal about the Royal Philosophers. Moreover, the Mitre Tavern, where the Philosophers met from 1743 to 1780, was the favorite tavern of Johnson, his refuge when things got too warm for him among his grotesque household of paupers in Fleet Street.

We find that Gibbon, Sterne, Boswell, Reynolds, and Dyer, among the early members of The Club, had been guests of the Philosophers, but there is no record that William Jones, Langton, Burke, Goldsmith, Garrick, or Bishop Percy had ever eaten with the scientific group. Samuel Dyer, it is interesting to find, had the honor of being one of the first members of both the Royal Philosophers, to which he was elected in 1758, and of The Club. He was "a man of profound and general erudition," according to Burke, and the author of the *Junius Letters,* according to Joshua Reynolds. He was a great favorite, but membership in the two dining clubs must have put a strain both on his wit and on his digestion. Of the others who were members of both clubs in the early days, I can find positive records only for Joshua Reynolds, Thomas Young, and Joseph Banks.

If the tavern was the Alma Mater of British science, it is no less true that English letters was nourished by it also. Shakespeare's degree was Master of Arts from Mermaid Tavern. The universities could have helped him little in his life as a dramatist, but at the Mermaid he could meet the world and live with it—he could learn of life from adventures on all the seas, and listen to the tales of stout travelers who had met danger in remote corners of the earth; Falstaff was merely local coloring. Some critics resent the tavern traditions associated with Shakespeare, but the story of the Royal Philosophers should make it easier to understand the part played by the English tavern in the life of a player and playwright. Men of science as well as poets and dramatists were vigorous men of the world, and their social gatherings could have been held in no more congenial home than an English inn. Both literature and science owe an unpaid and long delinquent tally on the slates of the London taverns.

It has been the custom of the Philosophers since 1743 to celebrate a so-called anniversary meeting in November of each year. In commemorating the one hundred and fiftieth anniversary at Limmers Hotel in 1893, it was arranged that the menu of 1747, described in the early part of this paper, should be reproduced and that the price should be the same, 1s, 6d. Among those present on the later occasion were such well known men as Sir Archibald Geikie, Lord Rayleigh, George Darwin, Francis Galton, William Crooks, James Dewar, A. G. Vernon Harcourt, and J. Norman Lockyer. That the spirit of the founders still prevailed in 1893 is proved by the fact that the Royal Philosophers were supplied with "Huff Ale" from Winchester College which had lain in bottles for ten years. The minutes record that the beverage was "potent" as well as "pleasant," and that Sir Andrew Noble had complimented the diners with a haunch of venison.

THE ROYAL PHILOSOPHERS

The most interesting days of the Royal Philosophers were those preceding the middle of the eighteenth century. I do not propose to follow their recent history. It is still, of course, a very honorable and a very distinguished club. In 1901 it absorbed another and more modern dining club, the Philosophical Club. The membership has been increased to over sixty, of whom thirty or more are usually present at its fortnightly meetings. It dines every second Thursday after the afternoon meeting of the Royal Society. The caliber of its nineteenth-century presidents and treasurers, Humphrey Davy, John Barrow, William Herschel, the Earl of Rosse, Benjamin Brodie, George Airy, Joseph Hooker, Thomas Huxley, George Gabriel Stokes, Lord Kelvin, Lord Lister, and William Huggins, shows that the club is not dying out. But I stand for the good old days, for the smaller group and the bigger "eats" and drinks; for the days of real adventure in science, when it took courage to doubt conventional truth, and when the four corners of the globe were yielding their first scientific truths. These were the days of general knowledge; they were big days for amateurs as well as for specialists. It meant something for such spirits to clash and to dine together. The modern age appears to be more serious. It approaches knowledge less light-heartedly. We are forced to believe that the convivial day of science has approached its twilight.

II

The Club

CLUBS are the children of the tavern, and taverns are the offspring of the manor house. This and other interesting facts I learn from a delightful book which has just come to my hand, Henry Parr Maskell's *The Taverns of Old England* (London, 1927). The lord of the manor, so the author explains, built his house in a conspicuous place near a village church, with its great hall and buhr and parlor arranged according to a conventional plan. In theory it was the residence of the landlord and his retainers, but in practice it was the public hall, the meeting place and administrative quarters of a community that was to a large extent self-governing under the presidency of its lord. Here were held the manorial courts which adjusted the holdings of lands within the manor and settled all sorts of minor matters. Here also, at Hocktide and at Harvest, were held the feasts which all the tenants would attend as their right, bringing wives, trenchers, cups, and napkins as their sole contribution.

Even on ordinary days a number of people lunched and dined in the great hall and afterward perhaps played various games. In the evening the trestled tables were cleared away and everybody settled himself to sleep on the rush-strewn floor. What few travel-

24

ers there were would be expected to report at the manor house; afterward they would take pot luck with the rest, unless their station in life entitled them to share the privacy of the parlor with the noble owner.

By the fourteenth century the aristocracy had ceased to live in the village and had withdrawn to more imposing country mansions. The manor house was left in the care of a steward, who found it convenient to add to his income by accepting gratuities. But to this day we still speak of the landlord; visitors are still called guests and are received by a hosteller; the buhr (or buttery), however, has become the bar, and the great hall has slowly and ignobly dwindled to a tap room. And even now, if your purse and your appearance justify it, you will receive the luxuries and the title of "The Gentleman in the Parlour." Perhaps it is not quite correct to suggest that in developing from the manor house the public house has become entirely different, for many of the original rights and dignities still remain, to which have been added the qualities of the inn. "Mine host" is still good English, and it is still good form for him to preside in person at the table. The hospitality of the manor house has come down to us, continuing in the customs of the public inn some of the amenities of early English life. It is a place where democracy is real—where all men are equal, and the duke may greet the dustman as a friend and brother without reproach. Here free speech is permitted to every man who can express himself without undue passion or violence. As of old, here come men of good will to exchange wisdom or confidences and to publish their ailments and woes; and here come strangers and pilgrims to find good company and good cheer; and here comes everybody to complain of the weather and to deplore the evil and degeneracy of the times. Here, too, come the homeless, the widow and the orphan, and they are not turned empty away. However the repute of the English public house may have fallen, it is still true that there is within its walls more genuine life than is open to the worldly rich at the Cecil, the Savoy, or the Metropole on the Embankment. We cannot ignore the influence of the tavern on British culture. It was a predecessor of, and a substitute for, the newspaper, the weekly journal, and the ponderous review. It became both a public and a literary forum and one of the nurseries of British liberty.

The origin of a particular tavern was usually revealed by its signboard. The arms of the noble family, for instance, would naturally appear on the public house situated on its own estates, and the houses in the royal manors became taverns bearing the sign of "The Crown." The religious houses had to be content with a different sort of crest, for, in theory at least, the church did not bear arms. The sign of "The Bull" was one of the boards commonly displayed by taverns on the manors owned by religious orders. Another, the sign of the "Pope's Head," had a sudden and ignominious end in 1534, in the reign of Henry VIII, when landlords who valued their heads hastily substituted for it the sign of the "King's Head." But the sign that most interests us is the "Turk's Head," which was, of course, the sign of a coffee house. Soon after 1650 the first London coffee house was set up in St. Michael's Alley in Cornhill by Pasqua Rosee, a Turk, at the sign of his own head. After the phenomenal success of Rosee's experiment, coffee houses sprang up everywhere, and the sign of the "Turk's Head" was standard equipment. Copies of Rosee's first advertisement are still in existence. It is a remarkable document. He states that "about a pint of it is to be drunk, fasting an hour before and not eating after, to be taken as hot as possibly can be endured. . . . It much quickens the spirit and makes the heart lightsome; it is good against sore eyes, and the better if you hold your head over it and take in the steam that way." The claim "good for sore eyes" made a hit and became a permanent part of our speech, a gift from faraway Turkey.

We should not neglect to say something about mine host, the proprietor of the tavern. As landlord, he not only ran away with the popular label of the lord of the manor, but he took with it many noble qualities to aid him in playing the part. Chaucer, of course, is our authority. The poet bestows upon "the Hoste" qualities that one would only hesitatingly ascribe to noblemen and kings. He was large and seemly, the fairest burgess of them all:

> *Bold of his speech and wise and well ytaught,*
> *And of manhood him lachede right naught.*
> *Eke thereto he was right a merry man.*

Chaucer, with his usual accuracy, paints a truthful picture of mine host, for in those days it was necessary that he be a man of great personal power and a natural leader if he expected to hold sway over his motley, and not too gentle, and ever changing stream of guests. It would do him no good to put his trust in the law or the police. He must have sense and judgment and be able to tell a saint from a sinner. He must possess the resourcefulness and the tact to meet a difficult situation on the instant. He must be tolerant and charitable and with enough humor to dispose him well with all sorts and conditions of men. In short, he must be a good sport and a good fellow.

Everybody knows of the tavern clubs of the days of Elizabeth and Shakespeare and Ben Jonson. James Buckles has left us a fine caricature. Writing about 1700 he said:

"Mr. B. invited me to his club at the Noah's Ark, where in a low room with an odor like a drunkard's morning's breath, several sat around the fire complaining of gouts, dropsies, pleurisies, palsies, rheumatisms, catarrhs, etc. till more company coming in, cryd to the table where one began his right hand's man's good health over the left thumb, which having gone around, the next was begun, and so they drank on till each had pledged everyman's health in the room. Many cups, many diseases. Too much oil chokes the lamp—But what followed? For wine immoderately taken makes men think themselves wondrous wise. Most of them became like Solomon's fool, full of words. What was it they said? E'en as what came uppermost: for as wine laid reason asleep each gave reins to his vanity and folly."

This picture is not unfaithfully drawn. It reveals the spirit of the tavern clubs—magic circles to which the guests brought their troubles and their woes, and soon reached a state of elation wherein the gloom of the world dissolved and discourse flowed in torrents. This was the ancestral form of club life, and the most exclusive and intellectual of modern clubs dare hardly deny their relationship to it.

Beaumont is more elusive than Buckles in his description of a club night. He pictures the elation of the gathered wits, but avoids resting any part of the intoxication on a physical base; yet the exhilaration was admittedly intense, even though you prefer to believe that it was purely spiritual. Addressing himself to Ben Jonson, he said:

> *What things have seen*
> *Done at the Mermaid; heard words that have been*
> *So nimble, and so full of subtle flame,*
> *As if that every one from whom they came*
> *Had mean'd to put his whole wit in a jest,*
> *And had resolv'd to live a fool the rest*
> *Of his dull life.*

ƒ

I AM WRITING in particular about The Club founded in 1764 by Joshua Reynolds, sometimes, but not correctly, called the Literary Club. It was one of the great grandmothers of modern dining and social clubs. As I have intimated, there is continuity in all things, and the laws of inheritance seem to apply more precisely to the institutions of men than to men themselves. But I am afraid that a modern club would hardly recognize itself in any of its great grandparents, nor could one of the ancient progenitors find many of the family features in us. To run true to type, we should seat ourselves about a great table in a London tavern. Our meal should be of heavy meats and pasties and our drink should be drawn from our own casks, aged in the tavern cellar, and the cost for the evening should be a guinea and a half for each of us.

Of all the numerous progeny of the English tavern, undoubtedly the longest lived and the most successful is the club known as the Royal Philosophers, which I describe elsewhere (page 3 above). About a century and a quarter after the birth of the Royal Philosophers, Joshua Reynolds, himself a Royal Philosopher, founded the famous group known as The Club. If Reynolds was the Romulus of The Club, Dr. Johnson was its Remus. Reynolds had long discussed the matter with Johnson, and both were equally responsible for the selection of the group of eight who constituted the first members. Edmund Burke and Oliver Goldsmith may be classified as friends of both Reynolds and Johnson. Two of the charter members were early and close friends of Dr. Johnson—Topham Beauclerk and Bennett Langton, Trinity College mates at Oxford. These were dipolar chums, however—Beauclerk being the worldly man of large property and Langton the man of much Greek learning—the positive and the negative or the negative and the positive poles, depending upon the end from which you view the world. The other original members were Dr. Christopher Nugent, M.D., a popular and most constant attendant, and Antony Charmier, a member of the Stock Exchange and later a public servant.

The group therefore consisted of four suns and four planets, Dr. Johnson being the giant star of the self-luminaries. The lesser men, however, were good fellows, clubable and gracious, most of them well traveled and some of them men of affairs. This sort of membership has been continued down to the present day. It has not been and is not a literary club, as it is often called and as it was dubbed by Boswell, but is composed of gentlemen of the world, taken from all walks of life—not long-faced specialists but good fellows, though men of "acknowledged literary taste." It is surprising how small a portion of the two hundred and ten members added to the original roll in the first century and a half of The Club history were really men of lasting repute. Important as many were in the affairs of their own day—the membership has included nine prime ministers, a score of bishops and archbishops, numerous much traveled and well-read Englishmen, and many noblemen of parts—only twenty-six can be classified as men of talent. The first elected member, Sir John Hawkins, was a failure. When the total reached twelve, as it did during the first year, he became a sort of Judas to the group, for after an evening of rude quarreling with Burke he seceded from The Club. It was for Hawkins that Dr. Johnson invented a new word, "unclubable," which has proved such a useful addition to our vocabulary. Notwithstanding this unfortunate beginning, six of the first twenty-five elected members were men of talent, a record reached on only one other occasion, when the membership had been increased to a total of thirty-six. These six, in the order of their admission, were David Garrick, James Boswell, Charles Fox, Edward Gibbon, Adam Smith, and Joseph Banks. We know definitely that it was Dr. Johnson himself who urged or rather ruthlessly forced Boswell upon The Club. Perhaps even then he had a vision of the immortality his crony was to attain:

Triumphant thou through Time's vast gulf shall sail,
The pilot of our literary whale.

This brings us down to 1778. Of the next twenty-five admissions, only one need be remembered, Edmund Malone, and the next group of twenty-five likewise contains but one distinguished name, Sir Humphrey Davy. It took forty years, from 1778 to 1818, to admit fifty additional members, and these were the least notable years in the history of The Club. Then a true revival took place. The next twenty-five names include Sir Walter Scott, Henry Hallam, Thomas Young, and William Buckland, all of whom were admitted within a period of ten years. From 1828 to 1857 twenty-five names were added, and although only two, Macaulay and Sir Richard Owen, were men of real distinction, these two were such unusual and enthusiastic members that their years of membership were years of prosperous Club life, preparing the way for a second revival in the years from

1857 to 1871. Among the twenty-five initiates of this latter period were Gladstone, Grote, Froude, Tennyson, Lord Salisbury, and Lord Acton. Death had been taking the older men, and the losses were now so heavy that twenty-five admissions were required in twelve years. Among these were John Tyndall, Lord Leighton, Matthew Arnold, and Thomas Huxley. Then The Club entered a duller cycle, only Lord Kelvin and Sir Richard Jebb the Greek scholar appearing as prominent names among the twenty-five which at the close of the nineteenth century ended the list of 200 elected members.

But the third Jubilee of The Club in 1914 was approaching, and this acted as a stimulus not only in reviving interest and pride in The Club, but in elevating the quality of the membership. Another result of the approaching anniversary was that the membership was for the first time brought up to the full number of forty. The elections filling these last vacancies are interesting because they show that there are two traits that work against election to membership—too much talent and too little talent. The following is an excerpt from the minutes:

"1914, March 3. The Treasurer reported that voting papers were issued for the following eight candidates: Mr. Charles W. C. Oman, Professor of Modern History at Oxford; Mr. Henry John Newbolt; Dr. Burge, Bishop of Southwark; Lord Seydenham; Viscount Bryce; Mr. John Murray; Mr. Rudyard Kipling, and Lord Sumner, Lord of Appeal, and that Viscount Bryce and Professor Oman had obtained the largest number of votes. A ballot was taken for them and they were unanimously elected. The Club then consisted of 37 members. It was resolved to hold a further election for two members. Voting papers to be issued and a ballot taken on April 21.

"April 21. The treasurer reported that three candidates had received an equal number of votes (12)—the Bishop of Southwark and Lord Sumner and Mr. Kipling. The members present decided by voting paper between the three, and the choice fell on the Bishop of Southwark and Lord Sumner, who were submitted to ballot and elected. The choice raised the members to thirty-nine, and it was decided to take a vote at the dinner of May 5 whether Mr. Kipling should be submitted forthwith to ballot.

"May 5. It was resolved to complete the membership up to forty. Mr. Kipling's name was submitted to ballot and he was unanimously elected."

Thus we have the interesting spectacle of Kipling becoming a member by the skin of his teeth and only under the pressure of preparation for the coming one hundred and fiftieth anniversary. Among the forty that may have sat with Kipling at the third Jubilee dinner, which was held just before the outbreak of the Great War, were the Earl of Rosebery, Sir George Trevelyan, Sir Edward Poynter, Lord Rathmore, Lord Lansdowne, Mr. Balfour, Mr. Asquith, Sir Edward Grey, the archbishops of York and Canterbury, the bishop of Oxford, Lord Hugh Cecil, Viscount Haldane, John S. Sargent, Earl Curzon, and twenty others filling up the rear ranks of The Club.

The attendance at the memorial dinner was about thirty. I do not have a copy of the roll of members present, but I do know that three prime ministers of Great Britain sat side by side—Lord Rosebery, Mr. Balfour, and Mr. Asquith, certainly an unusual sight. Since then Mr. Baldwin has been elected to membership, but not Messrs. Lloyd George and Ramsay MacDonald. Of the forty who were members in 1914 only fifteen now survive. The recent additions include the lord chief justice, the lord chancellor, the viceroy of India, Admiral Sir Herbert Richmond, the two bishops of Oxford, and the bishop of Durham, running rather heavily to titles and to purple, gold, and red drapery. Among the new members who are of interest to the university world are Dr. Montague James, provost of Eton; Dr. H. A. L. Fisher, warden of New College; Dr. F. W. Pember, warden of All Souls; Dr. A. S. Eddington, Plumian professor of astronomy, Trinity College, Cambridge; and the Right Honorable Sir Austen Chamberlain, who wears with greatest pride, of his numerous decorations, the robes of the Lord Rector of Glasgow University.

Monday was the original Club night and the dinner hour was 4:30; as time went on, the time was gradually advanced to 8:00, and the weekly meetings became fortnightly and were set for Fridays. The dinners were opened by pledging, each to each, The Club toast (attributed to Dr. Johnson): *Esto perpetua!*—Let it be perpetual! For twenty years The Club met at the Turk's Head on Gerrand Street, for sixty-three years at the Thatched House Tavern on St. James Street, for nearly forty years at the Clarendon, Albermarle Street, and for over twenty years at the Prince's Hotel, Jermyn Street. The attendance at the dinners has averaged only about eight and has tended to decrease rather than increase as the membership has been advanced from twelve to forty; there have been several meetings at which only two were present, and two or three memorable occasions when a single member dined alone—in 1825, for example, when the prime minister, Robert Jenkinson, made a club of one, and in 1908, when Lord Welby held forth in great state; he ordered two mirrors brought in, so that he could begin his right-hand man's good health over his left thumb. But the meetings are never abandoned, nor is one bit of the formality omitted because of small attendance.

For intimate knowledge of Club meetings and of Club affairs we must rely upon the letters and diaries written by members which comment on interesting discussions or quote good Club stories. The only officer of The Club is the treasurer, and the only minutes kept refer to finances and to the details of elections. Boswell makes several references to Club nights, but these are so familiar to you that I will not prolong this paper by quoting from them. Dr. Johnson early used his power to discourage formal talk or "talk from books" as he called it. He complained that Langton the Greek scholar and Garrick the actor "talked from books," and so great was his influence that the tradition was firmly established that the evening's discourse should be spontaneous and informal, free from highbrow mannerisms. Once when asked whether there had been much conversation at The Club, Johnson replied that "there had been talk but no conversation, there was not conversation without discussion." Toward the end of his life his interest in The Club began to wane. In a letter to Boswell he wrote: "It is proposed to augment The Club from twenty to thirty, of which I am glad, for, as we have several in it whom I do not much like to concert with, I am for reducing it to a mere miscellaneous collection of conspicuous men, without any determinate character." The Club as an intimate circle of congenial friends became hard to maintain. Hallam and Macaulay and Owen later did what they could to restore the original temper with considerable success. Macaulay knew what the original Club had been like; he is the source of the description of the early Club so often quoted:

"The club-room is before us, and the table on which stands the omelet for Nugent, and the lemons for Johnson. There are assembled those heads which live forever on the canvas of Reynolds. There are the spectacles of Burke, and the tall thin form of Langton, the courtly sneer of Beauclerk, and the beaming smile of Garrick, Gibbon tapping his snuff box, and Sir Joshua with his trumpet in his ear. In the foreground is that strange figure which is as familiar to us as the figures of those among whom we have been brought up, the gigantic body, the huge massy face seamed with the scars of disease, the brown coat, the black worsted stockings, the grey wig with the scorched foretop, the dirty hands, the nails bitten and pared to the quick. We see the eyes and mouth moving with convulsive twitches; we see the heavy form rolling; we hear it puffing; and then comes the 'Why, Sir!' and the 'What then, Sir?' and the 'No, Sir!' and 'You don't see your way through the question, Sir!' ''

Five years after the death of Dr. Johnson it was resolved by The Club that a monument be erected to his memory in Westminster Abbey, "the same to be a whole length statue of him in the ancient style of sculpture and that Sir Joshua Reynolds be requested to inquire of Mr. Bacon what will be expense of such a statue with all its proper accompaniments." To the cost of this monument, members contributed five guineas each, and by individual exertions secured the fine sum of eleven hundred pounds. After Reynolds' death in 1792 an attempt was made to secure for The Club a portrait of its co-founder, but it did not meet with the success which had attended the movement for a statue of Johnson. Nothing came of it, perhaps because there was no one left to exercise the leadership so long held by Reynolds. In 1801, however, the Marchioness of Thomond, a niece of Reynolds, was pleased to present a portrait of Reynolds copied from the original by himself, and it was ordered to be hung in The Club Room as a perpetual memorial of the much-lamented founder.

At the meeting held on February 26, 1805, the resolutions of February 28, 1792, relating to the statue of Dr. Johnson were read:

"Mr. Malone moved a resolution, seconded by Sir William Scott, 'that a subscription be entered into by this Club towards defraying the expense of the erection of a monument to the memory of Sir Joshua Reynolds, one of the Founders of The Club; the monument to be erected in St. Paul's Cathedral; the subscription to be five guineas each person, being the same sum that was subscribed by members of The Club for the monument of Dr. Johnson, our other founder. The members present this day agree to this resolution, which is left for the approbation of the other members of The Club. Mr. Malone will take the trouble to receive the subscriptions.' "

This action led to the gift of the well known monument in St. Paul's by Flaxman. It is generally agreed that Flaxman is the greatest of British sculptors. It is therefore deeply regrettable that he did not rise to the opportunity to create a masterpiece worthy of the founder of the Royal Academy.

The Club was a difficult place for anyone tainted with liberal political views; the only comfortable doctrines were those that were Tory and reactionary. It has always been a "hard-boiled" group. Both Fox and Gladstone had a difficult role to play, and each on several occasions found The Club atmosphere quite tense. There were too many puffy bishops and ponderous lords to permit liberal thinking in the concrete, even if it was mildly tolerated from time to time as a matter of abstract philosophy. It was not the loose conduct and the many private dissipations of Fox that caused him embarrassment at The Club, but his plan to limit the royal prerogative and extend the power of the House of Commons, and his persistence in discrediting the Bourbon regime in France. In 1793, after the French calamity, this is what happened to him at a club meeting, according to Dr. Burney, who wrote in his diary on January 29:

"At The Club on Tuesday, the fullest I ever knew, consisting of 15 members; 14 seemed all of one mind and full of reflections on the late transactions in France, but when about half the company was assembled, who should come in but Charles Fox! There were already 3 or 4 bishops arrived, hardly one of whom could look on him, I believe, without horror. After the first bow and cold salutation, the conversation stood still for several minutes. During dinner Mr. Windham and Burke junior came in, who were obliged to sit at a side table. All wore boutonnés, and not a word of the martyred king or politics of any kind was mentioned, and though the company was chiefly composed of the most eloquent and loquacious men in the kingdom, the conversation was the dullest and most uninteresting I ever remember at this or any such large meeting. Mr. Windham and Fox civil. Young Burke and he never spoke. The Bishop of Peterborough as sulky as the Devil. The Bishop of Salisbury, more a man of the world, very cheerful. The Bishop of Dromore frightened as much as a barndoor fowl at the sight of a fox. Bishop Marlay preserves his usual pleasant countenance. Steevens in the chair, the Duke of Leeds on his right, and Fox on his left, said not a word. Lords Ossory and Lucan, formerly much attached, seemed silent and sulky."

The feeling in Gladstone's later days was so tense

that Grant Duff, for many years treasurer of The
Club, in the brief biographies of deceased members
which he wrote in 1905, closed the account of Gladstone with the year 1868 and thought it necessary to
add these words at the end: "To carry his history
further in this book would be very undesirable. The
fires lie a great deal too near the surface."

The Club has shown no tendency to make membership a family prerogative. Burke had influence enough
to have his son Richard elected, but the young man
was such an ass and so unpopular with the others that
the precedent has rarely been followed. There have
been three very successful experiences of this sort,
however. Three much-loved members were the Bur-
neys—father, son, and grandson. Equally delightful
was the membership of the brothers Lyttelton, Spencer
and Alfred, who joined The Club in 1906 and 1908
and died in 1913, both in the same year. They were
the grandsons of the third Baron Lyttelton, who had
also been a member. Another family succession was
the case of the seventh and ninth earls of Carlisle. It
is the diary of the seventh earl that contains so many
intimate glimpses of The Club during the middle
years of the last century.

It is not easy to reconstruct The Club meetings from
the diaries of Carlisle and Grant Duff because of the
brevity of the entries. I must put upon the imagination of each of you the task of clothing with a little
flesh and blood the skeleton quotations I shall make.
Remember that for twenty years Macaulay was a
second Johnson to The Club and that Hallam, during

his thirty-six years of membership, was one of the most delightful members and helped make the reign of Macaulay complete. I quote a few entries from Carlisle's journal:

"February 5, 1849. A goodly company, but almost too many to make the most of all, and it is a pity for Macaulay and Hallam to sit together. It leads to a continued surge of talk between them which does not always break beyond. There was good talk, however. Cowper talked of as having been called the most popular of English poets; doubts whether he still holds that position."

"February 11, 1851. They talked of Gulliver, and of the Bishop who was taken in by it, but thought some parts must be exaggerated."

"1851. March 10. I cannot feel it to be a real Club dinner without Macaulay."

"1851. May 13. A good company. It was most agreeable. Praise of both Mure and Grote. They think Grote absurdly prejudiced in favour of all the Athenians did. They were very droll about Sir J. Sinclair, his writing to Pitt that it was very desirable that the President of the Scotch Agricultural Society, then appointed and paid by the State (he then holding it), should be a peer. Pitt answered he quite agreed with him, accepted his resignation, and appointed Lord Somerville. At the end the Bishop and I fought a mesmeric electrobiological battle against the scornful opposition of all the rest."

"1851. May 27. It was very pleasant, very literary. The talk ran for some time on whether the North or

South of different countries had contributed most of their literature. Overstone came in for a little talk about forestallers and regraters. The derivation of the last word could not be made out. If the Quakers were more numerous, Macaulay would exempt them from toleration, on account of their refusal to defend their country. I remained on with Macaulay and Milman. The first gave a list of 6 poets whom he placed above all others in the order of his preference: Shakespeare, Homer, Dante, Aeschylus, Milton, Sophocles. Milman on the whole acquiesced, but I believe he would place Milton next to Homer, above Aeschylus and him above Dante. I fought some battle for Virgil coming before Sophocles. He (Macaulay) would also place Lucretius and Ariosto before him. I urged the place which the general voice of mankind had given to Virgil. He thinks it can be accounted for. Dante could not read Greek, and Addison could not appreciate it. Virgil had written the best epic narrative among the Latin poets, whom he places below the poets of most nations. He thinks the homage to Virgil on the decrease."

"1852. March 22. Pleasant, but not quite so much as at times. One misses Macaulay. Milman doubts much, all did a little, whether the Mermaid or the Dolphin in Midsummer Night's Dream, was intended to be Mary Queen of Scots. I had not felt any doubts about it. They say Warburton first applied it to her. I asked them whether the word *universal* ought to have *a* or *an* before it. They were in favour of *an*, not very strongly. Talking of Jeffrey and his mincing

43

pronunciation, Lord Holland said it was not broad Scotch but narrow English."

"May 4, 1852. Very pleasant though select. Something led to my reminding Lord Aberdeen that we both put MacBeth the first of Shakespeare's great Plays . . . Lord Lansdowne quite concurred. Macaulay thinks it may be a little owing to our recollections of Mrs. Siddons. I asked as to the priority of composition. There is an edition of Hamlet in Elizabeth's time. Banquo's line was obviously intended as a compliment to James I. An edition of Shakespeare is still wanted. The first is now hard to read. He is proved to have been a man of substance, and to have been the most popular author of his day. He has left no panegyric whatever on any one else." Macaulay writes in his diary for this day: "Dined at The Club. We have taught Aberdeen to talk. He was quite gay."

"1853. February 15. The Bishop of London talked of the great improvement in education and in church attendance, particularly in Bethnal Green. He had established, while Bishop of Chester, some infant schools there against great opposition. He went in one day to see how the children were coming on. He found them making a great noise, and held up his finger to enjoin silence. Upon which they all shouted 'perpendicular.' "

"1858. March 23. We discussed the highest period of civilization and I think gave it to London at the present moment."

"1860. March 5. Hume the other day called Stafford O'Brien the 'member for Staffordshire,' apropos of which they mentioned his having said about some printed list that every 'name had an hysteric.' The House laughed. At last Dundas told him, 'We may hysteric in Scotland, but here they call it asterisk.' 'Do they—the fools.' It was remarkable agreeable; among others the Bishop. He told us two speeches of William 4 to him. At a large dinner: 'Ever since I came to the throne, I have liked to assemble at my table *all sorts of people*. Therefore, I now give you the health of the Bishop of London.' At another time the Bishop with the Archbishop of Canterbury to ask the King to subscribe to the National Society. William descanted on the defects of his own education, but he had now sown his wild oats, 'as I doubt not your Grace and your Lordship have done.' They mentioned that at a military dinner, sitting between Lord Fitzroy Somerset and Sir James Kemp, William eulogized the army on account of its comprehensive character: 'You, my Lord, have the blood of the Plantagenets in your veins. You, Sir James, are sprung from the very dregs of the People.' Dundas averred that no Scotchman had wit. Macaulay put in a plea for Burns. It seemed agreed that a good comedy had never come out of Scotland. The Bishop talked of the wit of Rowland Hill. One day his chapel, with a thinner attendance than usual, suddenly filled during a shower of rain. He said, 'I have often before heard of religion being used as a cloak, but never before as an umbrella.' In his later life he used to come to his Chapel in a carriage. He got an anonymous letter rebuking him for this. 'It was not the way his Heavenly

Master travelled.' He read the letter from the pulpit, and said it was quite true, but that if the writer would come to the vestry afterwards with a saddle and bridle, he would ride on him home."

The following brief notes are from the journal of Grant Duff:

"1891. April 7. Goschen quoted Bismarck on Haymerle, who always says *no,* repeating *no* when he awakes from sleep for fear he should have acquiesced in anything."

"1892. June 13. Acton said Napoleon put foremost among his opponent generals Alvinzi, whom he defeated at Arcola. Achmet Vefyk, Grand Vizier, married a slave. Layard asked him why. 'If I had married one of the great families I should have been troubled for patronage. Now every two or three years I give my father-in-law a pair of breeches and an oke of tobacco'."

"1898. May 17. Talk about what Johnson would have thought of present talk at The Club. Jebb thought that talk such as Johnson liked would be found at the Universities, not in the Common Rooms, but in men's rooms after they began to smoke."

"1898. June 21. Marquess or Marquis, which is correct? The King, said Penber, told Lord Salisbury's father on his attaining the marquisate, 'Remember you are an English marquess, not a French marquis.' "

"1899. June 13. Jebb asked Temple if it was true he had taught Mat. Arnold the logic necessary for the schools in an almost continuous sitting of twenty-six hours. Temple said it was true."

THE CLUB

"1900. March 6. Creighton puts Westminster Abbey above any other English Gothic. Maunde Thompson mentioned the drink, Mother-in-law—stout and bitter. It was told how Freeman in connexion with the Battle of Hastings, visited the grounds of Battle Abbey. A man came up and offered guidance. He was rather roughly repelled by Freeman. 'I don't want you. I have the leave of the Duke of Cleveland.' . . . 'But I am the Duke of Cleveland.'"

f

THE CLUB HAS never had a serious mission to perform nor any ulterior purpose. It has always been a perfectly useless institution. Its rivals in social prestige, the Society of the Dilettanti and the Roxburghe, are clubs which profess to have a useful existence. But on a Club night, after the courtesies and the toasts have been bountifully exchanged, and after the good stories have been told and a bit of literature or a piece of public business has been discussed, the meeting dissolves without having budged the world from its place, and, in turn, without having been jarred by it. The Club is not geared, even remotely, to the machinery of the things about it. Therefore this paper can contain no deep philosophy, nor can it contribute anything of permanent value. My aim has been merely to indulge in trivial gossip about a very worldly club. It is not even important whether serious or trivial matters be placed in the foreground of the picture, for that is a question of optics, depending upon the end from which you look at the thing. To serve the world you must also live with it—that is the way we were created, for we were constituted both an industrial and a convivial society. The Club, then, is essentially no more trivial than the Counting Room— the spot it occupies in your picture depends upon the geometry of your position. You may think that The Club is too large and that it has lost its intimate character and that it is quite artificially maintained and that it has far outlived its natural life. But it is difficult to sustain any of these points, since The Club itself claims to have no use and sets up no defense. There is nothing to do then but to join in the toast *Esto Perpetua!*

SOME MEN OF SCIENCE

Doing easily what others find difficult is talent; doing what is impossible to talent, is genius.—AMIEL

III

Polymaths: Technicians, Specialists, and Genius

IT WAS almost sixty years ago that Von Helmholtz began to lead Germany to a better industrial future and to guide her in the development of technical education. It is true that Germany possessed a number of good "polytechnicums," but their scientific and educational equipment did not meet the ideals of Helmholtz. He traveled about Germany preaching to the text "Science is the best technology," a slogan which he applied vigorously to the problem of the rapidly growing industry and technology of the new Germany. Professorships at the technical high schools were not then thought to be equal in honor to the professorships in the universities. Helmholtz believed that all sections of pure and applied science should advance abreast in unified formation and equal honor. No doubt he was envious of the dominant position of the Swiss Polytechnicum at Zurich.

The slogan "Science is the best technology" fixed the direction and the trend of Germany's ambition. About 1887 the Reichsanstalt was reorganized with Helmholtz at its head. That was a practical and concrete example of his policy. Helmholtz did not undervalue the services of technicians and mechanicians—he was one himself—but he believed that technicians had little to do with technology. Technology, to be worth while, must be indistinguishable from science, and the practitioner must first of all be trained and inspired by the methods of science. Technique there must be, but the kind of technique so general at that date, both in medicine and in engineering, based primarily on rule of thumb and current practice, he regarded lightly. He directed his influence against the empirical concept of technology and the growing narrowness of the specialists. Helmholtz was familiar with more than one great field of learning. He taught the lessons he had learned from the vast variety of his experience and from his profound knowledge of the history of science.

IN ANCIENT times, of course, all engineers were scientists, and all scientists were masters of many fields. The etymology of the word *mathematics* illustrates this. *Mathematics* does not mean mathematics; it means science or, more accurately, general science or all science. Nevertheless, and perhaps unfortunately, there is such a thing as specialization, and also such a thing as narrow specialization. We not only have scientists, we have chemists. We not only have chemists, we have colloid chemists. We not only have colloid chemists, we have inorganic colloid chemists. We not only have inorganic colloid chemists, we have areosol inorganic colloid chemists. We not only have areosol inorganic colloid chemists, we have high temperature areosol inorganic colloid chemists, and so on indefinitely until the scientist is fractionated to a single paragraph of his doctor's thesis. Science has become an asylum with many cells and with many minute padded cubicles for the violent cases. But nature is constantly breaking all bonds; she delights in liberating supermen to whom she gives freedom to pace all the corridors of knowledge. Aristotle gave devotion to all the philosophies. Such a man we call a *polymath*, again using the root meaning present in the word mathematics. The ages have given us many polymaths and not a few in whom technology and pure science have been joined together.

It is Archimedes, of course, who should be canonized as the patron saint of scientists, as well as the patron saint of engineers. He it was who first announced the principle of moments and the properties of the center of gravity. This alone would make him the Adam of the engineering paradise, for many a modern engineer makes his living from the principle of moments alone, as Helmholtz delighted to observe. But of course Archimedes did more than that. He was the wizard of the ancient world—the Newton, the Einstein, the Edison, the Marconi of his day, both in fact and in popular acclaim. When he exclaimed, "Give me a place to stand and I will move the world," he was speaking as an engineer, with the customary self-confidence and brusque assurance of that profession. At his death, when he was surprised in his study by the Roman soldier, it was not Archimedes the engineer but Archimedes the scientist who spoke and begged the Roman to stay his sword for a moment so that he might bring his demonstration to bear and not leave his theorem incomplete. We should canonize this martyr as the patron saint of both science and technology. In the cathedral of science I suggest two chapels: one to Saint Archimedes the patron of engineers, with a painting above the altar showing him boldly demanding a place to stand that he might displace and disjoint the earth; and another to Saint Archimedes the patron of science, with a panel above the altar depicting him face to face with his murderer, pleading that his thought be not left imperfect.

Many of you probably hold views concerning human ability that I am too old-fashioned to understand. You probably accept the latest theory that genius is not made nor even possessed by the individual, but is the gift of the public and the creation of humanity at large. Shakespeare, Napoleon, and the others were not supermen in themselves, but only the creatures of their own and the following generations. But if I confine myself to the presentation of verbal pictures, you, with your modernistic philosophy, can draw the proper conclusion, and I, with my old-fashioned ideas, can adhere to my ancient philosophy. A few of you may embrace both views, contradictory though they are, and allot to every superman the share that is his own and also the part that the world has produced in him. Compromise in contradictions is a much practiced modern art.

As we run down the centuries from the apostolic age of Archimedes, we arrive at that amazing galaxy of polymaths which characterized the Renaissance.

Leonardo seemed to know and to be able to do every-thing; his attainments are so well known that I will not detain you with their consideration. But there were many others who were almost as polymathical. It was a common thing for a man to start out in a career quite remote from science and to be rescued later by an irresistible impulse, often originating in a trivial incident. Euler was destined for the church, but switched to medicine, then to mathematics. James Bernoulli was to have been a clergyman; John Bernoulli started out as a business man; and Daniel Bernoulli actually became a physician and was at one time professor of anatomy and botany at Basel. John Wallis the mathematician was the prosperous rector of St. Martin's ultra-fashionable parish and the author of the best English grammar of his time.

Sir Christopher Wren, known to every schoolboy as a prodigy of universal science, is the man whom we all would bracket with Leonardo for a first prize in polymathics. He was professor of astronomy at Oxford and an original experimenter in anatomy and physiology and in the transfusion of blood from one animal to another. He was complimented by Newton for his mastery of mathematics. He was the originator of a microscopic study of insects. He was an artist and a poet and for twenty years a member of parliament. His side lines were a complete plan for the rebuilding of London after the great fire of 1666, the construction of the military defenses of the city, the architecture of halls and towers at Oxford and Cambridge, and the building of St. Paul's Cathedral.

Newton had more fun in the thirty years that he was warden and master of the mint and busy revising the king's coinage than he had had during his thirty years on the faculty of Cambridge. Helmholtz started his career in medicine and physiology and found that this preparation won him a unique position in physics. Thomas Young the physicist and mathematician was the leading physician of his day, with medical degrees from Edinburgh, Göttingen, and Oxford, the best-dressed man in Bond Street, and the social favorite of the ladies. He was a linguist and Orientalist and the first scholar to decipher the Egyptian hieroglyphics. Lagrange had planned a literary career, and Huyghens started life as a lawyer. Some geniuses have been polyglots as well as polymaths. Hamilton had mastered four languages at the age of four (including the *Iliad* of Homer) and ten more at the age of fourteen. Euler was a notable linguist and literary critic and had so keen a memory that total blindness neither stopped his studies nor interfered with his most complicated calculations. Perhaps most curious of all is the case of that foundling who called himself D'Alembert. He studied all three professions—divinity, medicine, and law; was a musician, a writer, and a critic of note; and a philosopher and conversationalist welcomed in all the brilliant salons of his day.

Men of multiplex genius like these have no trouble in solving engineering and technical difficulties, and many of them have been great inventors. Huyghens invented the pendulum clock and the coil spring, and Euler won a prize on the masting of ships. The thing that genius seems to need most is a challenge—it matters not whether it comes from pure or applied science or from the perplexities of church or state. You will agree, I think, that inventiveness is not a departmental trait and that the imagination of men does not naturally explore in definite paths or lines, but has a tendency to spread and expand in all dimensions of knowledge.

ƒ

IN WHAT follows I shall adopt the plan of Plutarch and present the substance of my discourse through the media of two contrasting characters. The first of these is Lord Kelvin, or Sir William Thomson, as he was known for much of his life. When I was a college student and was constantly required to study Thomson and Tait, I must confess that I felt little enthusiasm or affection for the man or his book. The treatment of the same topics in the French treatises was so much more elegant and so much more lively that Thomson and Tait seemed dry, and the personalities back of the writing hardly seemed real. But in later years I discovered that Lord Kelvin was one of the most human and most lovable of characters, one who never lost his youthfulness nor his simplicity and naturalness of spirit. His nervous ecstasies in discovery and his delight in invention and mechanical devices were always those of a boy. He never outgrew the enthusiasms of his college days.

Lord Kelvin was fortunate in his early training, for his father, professor of mathematics at Glasgow, had no small part in giving a modern trend to his son's scholarship. It was a time when it was not the fashion to give much attention to what was going on in science on the continent of Europe. Cambridge was self-satisfied and self-sufficient in the conduct of the Mathematical Tripos, which it was content to retain as a gentleman's game quite insulated from the new learning. The Tripos, like fox hunting or polo or cricket, was to be taken most seriously, of course, for sport is the most serious of all human efforts: your wife will bear me out that a misplayed card in your bridge is much more serious than a misplaced syllogism in your logic. And so the game of the Tripos was not permitted to share in the joy and the adventure and the freedom of productive scholarship. A century ago Cambridge knew how to play the mathematical game to perfection, and even today the reform of the Tripos is not perfect. But James Thomson, father of Lord Kelvin, was bound by no examination tradition. The son of a small farmer of County Downs, he was too poor to afford anything better than Glasgow University and even then he was late in entering. Thus he was able to short-circuit the Cambridge conservatism.

The early nineteenth century was a prosperous and exciting time in mathematics: analytical methods were superseding others, and the general superstructure of analysis was being carefully fabricated. Laplace was at the height of his fame, Legendre had written memoirs which were to lead, in the hands of Jacobi and his successors, to a new domain of science, and "Gauss had begun his stately march of discovery." The world was ready for a new group of adventurers—Poisson, Fourier, Cauchy, and others. The memoirs and treatises of these continental writers James Thomson eagerly procured and studied; he had escaped the Cambridge cramps. At twenty-nine he was professor at Belfast and in 1832, at forty-six, he was called to the chair at Glasgow. He was free in his teaching, textbooks, and other writings to make continental mathematics known to his students and to the English public. His children, William and James, learning from him at Glasgow, early became aware that there were mathematicians later than Euclid and Newton and that they were as a matter of fact living in an exalted epoch of the exact sciences.

The seven years from 1834 to 1841 William spent at the University of Glasgow. The temper of the University of that day is sufficiently described by the fact that it was the university of Adam Smith, James Watt, and Thomas Reid. The quality of the training it offered to young Thomson is illustrated by an incident that occurred in the summer of 1840, when the sixteen-year-old lad was making a tour of Germany with his father and his brother James. Before leaving England they had agreed that all study except that of German was to be taboo. But William had just begun Fourier's *Theory of Heat*. Surreptitiously he took the book with him and in a fortnight had finished it. He concluded that an attack on Fourier by Professor Kelland was unjustified, and the discovery required him to confess his sin to his father. He was promptly forgiven, and from Frankfort he sent to the *Cambridge Mathemat-*

ical Journal his first paper on Fourier's method, which was soon followed by a second.

The next year, at seventeen, he entered Cambridge, where he at once became a great favorite and made many lifelong friends. In sports he won the silver sculls and many other trophies and contributed the tooting of the French horn to the CUMS. Ten papers, all on the flow of heat, appeared during his first two years at Cambridge. He was the much discussed favorite for Senior Wrangler, but he had put too much time on the mechanics of Laplace and Lagrange and hence surprised his friends and even the Moderators by taking Second Wrangler. Notwithstanding this concession to the Cambridge system, a few days later he became Smith Prizeman and won a fellowship. That summer he visited Faraday in London and spent the rest of the summer in the laboratory of Regnault in Paris. Then, only a year after graduation, he was called to the chair of natural philosophy at Glasgow, a position he was destined to hold for more than fifty years. He now had the freedom he long had coveted; the famous wine cellar at the old university became the first laboratory of physics in Britain and probably the first laboratory in the world open to undergraduates.

At that time the great job to be accomplished was the substitution of quantitative for qualitative work in nearly all domains of physics. It is difficult to realize now how primitive was the state of affairs at that time. Ampère would give measurements of electrical resistance in terms of a piece of copper wire kept in his laboratory. No one could check or compare his work with another. The new professor at Glasgow was soon making a beginning in the design of a variety of quantitative instruments, many of which were destined to make him both wealthy and famous. For Thomson was by nature an engineer; he wished to make things work and be of use. The improvement in telegraphy and the hot discussion over the possibility of submarine telegraphy absorbed his attention. There was much difference of opinion on the subject, especially concerning the electric voltage that should be used. Fortunately Thomson's low voltage ideas won the day, and when the first Atlantic cable was laid he was not only responsible for the design of the cable and its instruments of test and operation, but was on board ship throughout the laying of this cable and its two successors.

In these early years, as chief engineer of the cable company, he helped in everything that had to do with the project, such as the design of grappling hooks, splicing tools, and tension control. This is not the place to give the history of the early cables, but it may be remarked that no one without the perseverance of the English could have been successful. The first two cables from the Azores to Brazil were a total loss, the one being lost just as the Brazilian shore was reached, and the other going down with ship and crew when partly laid. For many years the laborious manufacture of the cables received the personal supervision of Chief Engineer Thomson. A compartment in the night London Express was always held for him, and the famous train was often kept waiting for special apparatus from White's, the instrument-maker. Kelvin commuted frequently between Glasgow and London in the interest of the cables and his engineering devices, such as the famous compass for steel ships and the sounding apparatus. Personally he pushed the sale of these with the shipping interests, fought for their adoption with the bureaucrats of the navy, and actively defended the patents in court. He was willing to patent anything. As a result he became very wealthy, partly from his share in the companies making the cables, instruments, and other devices. His fame among the common people was due in great part to his invention of a water tap known as the Kelvin Tap. Millions who would never have heard his name except for this non-leakable contraption knew him for that. He was shocked and indignant when his friends joked with him about it, for he thought a non-leakable tap quite as important for many people as a mirror electrometer, and he was delighted to be thought clever enough to invent a good household device.

His example and his public utterances express an attitude toward engineering quite the obverse of that of Helmholtz. At an address before the Institute of Electrical Engineers in 1883, for instance, his text was, "The life and soul of science is its practical application." This dictum does not exactly deny that "science is the best technology," but it at least puts the Helmholtz saying in reverse. The millionaire inventor of a water tap could hardly say less. But Kelvin was essentially a mechanical philosopher. He sought mechanical models for all his concepts and for all the phenomena of science. Although a deeply religious man in the conventional sense, no naturalist of his century adhered more fanatically to a mechanical explanation of the nature of things. When the new physics was putting forth its new and almost mystic conceptions during the last years of Kelvin's life, he became a vigorous and bitter opponent of the new ideas. Although he lived until 1907, he never accepted Clerk Maxwell's electrical theory. He fought Rutherford and all his modern theory of radio-activity. To him all phenomena were strictly mechanical—he could think only in terms of springs and wheels and gadgets.

In all his many activities and throughout the preparation of his prolific scientific writings, Kelvin the man was always dominant. He never ceased scientific productivity for a moment. At his country estate at Netherall there was as much good science in incubation as at Glasgow. Even on his large yacht, the *Lalla Rookh,* there was always science in the making and, as at Netherall, he often had assistants with him. He was never without his specially made large green notebook, for which he had game pockets put in the back of all his coats; every year he filled several of these "green books." Science to him was play, and it was always mixed with his other play. His favorite pets, his dog and his parrots, shared his research with him. Parrots are notoriously long lived, but it took two of them, Doctor Hookbeak and Doctor Redtail, to outlast Lord Kelvin. A favorite diversion at Netherall was to dictate to two secretaries on two different scientific topics at once and at the same time conduct a singing lesson for Doctor Redtail. The parrot, however, was quite as much attracted to the asides made under his breath by the faithful butler as to the formal lessons of the master, and the dinner guests were often shocked, upon the late arrival of the host at table, to hear Doctor Redtail exclaim, "Late again, Sir William, old boy!"

I doubt if anyone has ever received as many honors or as many memberships in scientific and engineering societies, or been as universally acclaimed, as has Lord Kelvin. The universities exhausted their honorary degrees. Even the University of London, which had never conferred an honorary degree, felt obliged to make an exception. Heidelberg, looking over Kelvin's long list of honors, hit upon the happy novelty of conferring on him the degree of doctor of medicine. This certainly ought to give Lord Kelvin a standing among the polymaths.

f

WHILE KELVIN was building his scientific and worldly fortune and amassing his honors and decorations, another great Englishman was working in almost complete seclusion, remote from centers of learning and unknown and unrecognized by the society he was serving. Kelvin came from a family of scientists, Oliver Heaviside from a family of engineers. His uncle was Wheatstone, the founder of practical telegraphy, and his father and brother were among its early promoters. Soon after leaving school Heaviside obtained a post with the Great Northern Telegraph Company, which he held for several years. During this period he contributed papers to the *Telegraphic Journal* and to the *Philosophical Magazine,* papers that were much above the average in ability and originality. In 1873, for example, he showed that quadruplex telegraphy was possible, but he took out no patents, nor did it ever occur to him to profit from his profound studies.

The next year, at the early age of twenty-four, increasing deafness required him to retire, and he spent the rest of his life as a scientific hermit at Torquay, devoting himself to mathematical studies in electricity and its applications. Gradually his papers became more and more technical, more and more exacting, and more and more difficult to understand. At a time when all of Lord Kelvin's writings were being accepted by the scientific journals, even lecture notes compiled primarily for his students and many long papers which unfortunately did no more than repeat the conclusions of others, the hermit of Torquay was having the greatest difficulty in securing publication of his work. Few editors or referees of the technical journals were competent to understand them. Hence the editors required his papers to be cut, with the result that many necessary and elegant mathematical links were left out and the work so mutilated that it was difficult to follow and to appraise. Fortunately one or two scientists, notably Oliver Lodge and John Perry, had discerned here a mathematical physicist of superior talent, and through their aid some of his best work was saved from the waste basket. Heaviside communicated to the Society of Telegraph Engineers (now the Institute of Electrical Engineers) a paper solving the problem of the electrostatic and electromagnetic interference between overhead parallel wires. In 1887 he published his method of measuring mutual inductance. He was the first to solve the problem of high-frequency resistance and inductance of a concentric main. In the realm of the practical, he laid the foundation of the modern theory of telephonic transmission, a theory that has proved a veritable gold mine for the practical worker in telephony. He showed that the difficulties arose from the different attenuations and velocities of the component waves which carry the currents. He showed on what lines undistorted waves could be transmitted. He let others take out the patents and mine the gold. In money matters Kelvin was true to his Scotch inheritance. Heaviside said that the question, Will it pay? never interested him. He wished to be known, he said, as a "philanthropist"—a free giver of the best that was in him. His work has saved every civilized country millions of dollars in the cost of its telephonic and wireless developments. While all England was acclaiming Kelvin and he numbered his friends by the scores of scores, the only intimate scientific friend of Heaviside was Dr. Searle of Cambridge.

For more than a generation, alone and almost unnoticed, Heaviside lived in his villa at Torquay on the pension of two hundred pounds which had generously been awarded him by the Royal Society. The oaken door of his mansion was nailed with numerous notices of executions for nonpayment of taxes and similar delinquencies. A few times a week a woman of the countryside brought him milk and simple food and his laundry. He was always carefully groomed and immaculate in his linen and broadcloth of the seventies. But this aristocratic and handsome figure did not seem alone, nor did he feel a grudge against an unappreciative world. On the walls of his study were hundreds of portraits of the scientific worthies of his century, and endless stacks of books seemed to constitute the framework of the house itself. Through the windows there entered at all hours the matchless beauty of the bay and the curving shores of Torquay, and all the changing lights that the sun and the moon and the clouds and the waves could mingle for his sensitive and appreciative eyes. There on the tables and shelves were the visible results of a busy and devoted life—thousands of pages of unpublished manuscripts, a serial record of many happy hours. Now the Royal Society has these papers, and from them, the editors say, we shall learn much of the foundations of his scientific processes which have heretofore been so darkly hidden in the skeleton outlines printed in his lifetime. But it is gratifying to know that in his last years he was one whom every electrical engineer delighted to honor. He received the first Faraday medal and many other laurels. His reputation today, seven years after his death, is growing apace. To verify all of Heaviside's reasoning and to examine and explore the validity of his mathematical methods will provide ample work for many mathematicians and physicists. He himself took his greatest satisfaction in the discovery of the increase of mass of a moving electric charge and in the prediction of the existence in the atmosphere of what we now call the Heaviside layer.

The deafness of Heaviside prevented him from attending scientific meetings and from receiving the benefit of the advice and stimulus of fellow workers. Lord Kelvin attended every meeting from beginning to end. He was always bobbing up in multifarious discussion with the activity of an irrepressible small boy at a birthday party. No meeting seemed quite the same after his death.

There was no debate about the burial place of Lord Kelvin. He was entombed at Westminster by the side of Newton. No such public honor could, of course, be expected for the hermit of Torquay. Nevertheless, as the years roll on, the power and the originality of Heaviside's work emerge more and more. Perhaps, after all, the popular judgment concerning these contrasting characters may not be infallible nor final. We may be sure that the popular acclaim of the one, and the public neglect of the other, will have little to do with the ultimate appraisal of their scientific worth. In the long record of Time's reversals of contemporary judgments, we may yet read that Kelvin, the mathematical physicist, is assigned final honor primarily for his engineering courage in the development of submarine telegraphy, and that Heaviside, the electrical engineer, is awarded immortality for his sagacity in mathematical discovery. Time is the greatest of all jurists. Its judgment in this matter has not yet been handed down.

♪

HAVE THE days of the polymath come to an end? Can scientists of the all-embracing interest and accomplishment of Saint Archimedes continue to flourish? The popular answer seems to be no; this is the age of specialists. But closer examination does not lead to this conclusion. The modern specialist is a manufactured product. We make each year the number of specialists our civilization requires. We produce, say, twenty thousand machinists, ten thousand engineers, seven thousand lawyers, five thousand physicians, three thousand doctors of philosophy. If the demand is greater, we produce more. We produce chemists and engineers and physicists and lawyers to equal the demand.

But above the specialists and all the human merchandise of university mass production, there is another group, masters of knowledge like Kelvin, Helmholtz, and Heaviside. These are not manufactured nor standardized products. Of these there are never enough and the supply is beyond our control. And above these masters are the men of true genius, men like Archimedes, Newton, Laplace, Darwin, Einstein. This group is unique and individual in its last characteristic. One of them is equally likely to appear as a polymath or as a genius of narrow form, just as nature happens to decide, and quite as likely in the present age as in ages past. The specialist deals in facts, multiplied without end. The genius deals not in facts, but in perplexities and contradictions and paradoxes. Darwin was a genius not because he industriously accumulated an encyclopedia of facts, but because of the philosophical revolution he brought about by his spiritual and almost mystical interpretation of those facts. Kelvin conformed to conventional truth; to him no great novelty of thought was tolerable. The then existing mechanical principles constituted the true faith worthy of all men to be believed—even the electrical theory of Clerk Maxwell must be bitterly opposed as unorthodox and dangerous. Genius challenges conventional truth. It invokes allegiance to unrealized principles, to principles that often must be fought for at great risk. The fundamentals of knowledge in any age are few, not infinite, in number—so few, perhaps, that a polymath may uncover and master all of them. These are the men whom each age awaits, but who appear only at culminating epochs in the affairs of men. Their mission is to question certainties, to "doubt all things that can be doubted," and to bring us mysteries. It is something of life to learn that there are mysteries that shadow it; it is something of life to know that there are truths still hidden even from the prophets.

But these are old-fashioned views, and I should not urge them upon you. In the modernistic scheme of things supermen are the creation of the multitude, and you can contend that the contrasting characters I have presented to you prove the case. What does it matter if Kelvin could not find his way into the new conceptions and mysteries of modern science? Did he not amass a fortune? Was he not universally acclaimed and decorated? Was he not knighted and raised to the peerage and buried in Westminster? The Cathedral of Science is not made of stone, but is a vision, perhaps an hallucination, of the public. It matters little to whom we dedicate its immaterial chapels—saints or sinners, simple men or supermen. It is only our belief and our concerted faith that counts. If we light the candles before a favorite altar, there seeking to be refreshed and sanctified, it matters only that the place be dedicated to one who the crowd claims has attained unto glory and who our faith declares to be worthy of adoration.

The contrast between the two characters I have presented extended even to their spiritual lives. To Kelvin religion was a concrete and orthodox and bounded central zone, surrounded by a vast expanse of scientific truth, which to him was the world of reality. To Heaviside all of this stood in reverse: science was a growing, but shifting, central area, a make-believe world, circumscribed by a border of mystery, beyond which lay an endless spiritual domain, to him the true world of reality. In his solitude at Torquay his eyes met first the curving shores of the sea, then the rhythmic pulsing of the waters, fading away to the rim of the horizon, on and on into the haze, but emerging again, clearer and clearer to his inner sense, into a spiritual realm of reality.

Heaviside knew that there are Two Worlds.

*One is the World of Science, which Kelvin so
naïvely and so falsely deemed the World of Reality.*

*For the room of this world, man imagines a Space,
and, in the space, a Frame of Reference for
Events.*

*To mark an event, he makes an Arrow, happily
called Time's Arrow, for he says it leads from
that which now is to that which is to come.*

*The arrow is trued and checked against the frame,
and the trend of the arrows he calls Causality,
and the metrics of the arrows are the measures of
science.*

*To this make-believe world, man adds the artifacts
and the imaginings and the changeful theories of
science and also the Averages of many measures.*

*He writes down his findings and in his audacity
calls them the Record of the Nature of Things.*

*All of this and nothing more makes up the World
of Science.*

*Heaviside knew that there is a greater world, the
World of Personality.*

*The room of this world is not the frigid space of
science, but the warm continuum of the Great
Presence.*

*Within this world is fixed a three-fold frame:
Truth, Beauty, Virtue.*

*Also, for each personality, there is a Time's Arrow
—a Golden Arrow—trued and checked against*

the frame of Truth, Beauty, Virtue, and the trend of the arrows we call Purpose.

The metrics of the arrow are not the measures of science, but the countings and weighings of Spiritual Values.

The Great Presence is mindful of the arrow, for as that golden vector moves and orbits in a spiral of life, there exists a Best Way and many less perfect ways, and the Great Presence would guide and shield that orbit in the way that is best and lead it more and more to its own perfect purpose.

This is the spiritual creed of evolution, and it holds alike for galaxies and for men.

At last, for each of us, the World of Science crashes and comes to naught again, and we call it Death.

But the world of the Great Presence does not end, for the golden arrow courses on, still trued to the frame of Truth, Beauty, Virtue, on and on into the most traveled and best-known domain, which we so naïvely and so falsely call the Great Unknown.

This is the domain searched by philosophers and prophets, by Plato and Saint Paul and all the saintly mystics.

This domain to Heaviside was, in truth, the World of Reality.

IV

The Principia and the Modern Age

THE beginning of a unified conception of the universe was not made by mathematicians. It was the discovery of poets. That is to say, the first approach to nature was esthetic, not scientific. Over two thousand years ago Solomon is reported to have acknowledged his God in these words: "He hath given me the certain knowledge of the things that are, namely to know how the world was made, and the operation of the elements; the beginning, ending, and the midst of the times; the alterations of the turning of the sun, and the change of seasons; the circuit of the years and the position of the stars: . . . And all such things as are either secret or manifest, them I know."

These are strong words from Solomon. His enthusiasm seems to have outrun his modesty. Only poets can indulge in such overweening self-confidence. They call it inspiration. Sometimes I think it is as sound an approach to reality as any other.

One might conclude from the words attributed to Solomon that he and not Newton had written the *Principia*. But Newton in his modesty made no such claim as did Solomon. He was only a child gathering a few pebbles on the shore of a vast sea. Solomon's words, sympathetically interpreted, mean that his approach to nature was esthetic—an approach by faith

74

which is open to everyone, whether a person of little or of much sagacity. Solomon was expressing his belief in the wisdom of a single author of the world and was giving vent to his ecstasy over the harmonies and beauty of created things. He was rebuking and setting himself against those of his day who believed in a multitude of gods or demons, who saw an individual god back of each manifestation of nature. "Surely vain are all men," he said, ". . . who could not, out of the good things that are seen, know him that is; who by considering the works, did not consider the work master, but deemed either fire, or wind, or the swift air, or the circle of the stars, or the violent water, or the lights of heaven, to be the gods that govern the world." A single God, "the first author of beauty," as he so happily called him, "ordered all things in measure and number and weight."

In his *Principia* Newton sought to discover and set forth the exact manner in which "all things had been ordered in measure and number and weight."

To understand the *Principia,* one must first recall something of the times in which it was written and the temper of the group of young English scientists which gave character to the age in which Newton was born. The *Principia* must be looked upon as the masterpiece born of the new learning or experimental philosophy that took its hold on the world about three centuries ago. The old learning was resting quietly in the universities of Oxford and Cambridge. Aristotle and the seven philosophies seemed safe and fixed and unchangeable. Then from outside the universities an intellectual revolution got under way. Bacon had announced that the methods employed in the sciences and the results reached were alike erroneous, "yielding," he said, "no true fruit of learning." A new method of philosophy must be devised, he said, whose aim should be to serve men rather than merely to give pleasure and delight to scholars. The world was ripe for Bacon's ideas, and they probably would have burst forth even without his powerful aid. Within twenty years of his death a group of vigorous young men in London had taken up the new philosophy. The first home of the new learning was the ever hospitable London tavern. This may seem a strange place for the birth of the new learning, but it was natural enough. Private homes were for the most part poorly built, uncomfortable and cold. The taverns were warm and cheery and the center of life and hospitality. Hence it was quite natural that in 1645, three years after the birth of Newton, we should find a group of diners meeting regularly at the Bull-Head Inn in Cheapside to discuss and experiment in the new philosophy.

As we have described elsewhere, it was this group, called by Boyle the "Invisible College," that in 1660 organized the "Visible College," chartered as the Royal Society of London for the Improvement of Natural Knowledge. In that charter the King said: "We do hereby make and constitute the said Society . . . to be a Body Corporate . . . whose studies are to be employed for the promotion of the knowledge of natural things and useful arts by *Experiments*." On this foundation has been built the great structure of British science. It was the age of scientific revolution. Experimentation became a craze, and natural science developed outside the universities and in spite of them. The newly founded Gresham College in London was an exception. It is renowned chiefly for having become, in the first fifty years of its life, the home of the new philosophy. Not only was it the cradle of the Royal Society, but its fine halls were the meeting place of the Society for nearly the first half century of its history. Its galleries housed its libraries and curiosities and supplied the permanent offices for the secretaries and officials of the new society.

The men who constituted these first groups of organized science were not long-faced specialists nor academicians in the continental sense, but convivial Englishmen from all walks of life. This type of membership was maintained for many generations. The membership lists for the first century of the Royal Society include many prominent members of the peerage, numerous members of parliament, amiable and versatile politicians, a notable band of medical men, artists, critics, civil servants, and pamphleteers. There were bishops and explorers and travelers and antiquarians and many all-round good fellows whose principal job was to contribute enthusiasm and financial support. This was the world of scientific enthusiasms into which Newton was born, and these were the men from whom were drawn his colleagues and worshippers.

The interesting partnership between English men

of the world and English scholars in promoting the new philosophy is emphasized when we join together such names as Samuel Pepys and Isaac Newton, both of whom served as president of the Royal Society within an interval of twenty years. Newton became a fellow of the Royal Society in 1672 and thirty years later its president; Pepys became a fellow in 1664 and president in 1684.

Newton's name, moreover, is immortalized with Pepys' in another and very interesting manner. The Royal Society not only issued printed transactions from time to time, but it also undertook to print, at its own expense, meritorious scientific books and treatises. It thus came about in 1687 that *Philosophiae Naturalis Principia Mathematica* was brought out by the Royal Society. On the title page we read: "I. Newton, he wrote it," and below this, "Samuel Pepys, President Royal Society, he printed it." This was a remarkable linking of the names of two very different men. Newton, as we all know, was a man of temperate and abstemious habits who led a simple life quite devoid of even the conviviality enjoyed by nearly all his associates. Pepys was an example of the animalism of the seventeenth century.

But the title page does not tell the whole story. The Royal Society, it is true, had promised to publish the book, but it was actually Halley the astronomer who furnished the funds from his own meager purse. It is difficult to exaggerate the indebtedness of the world to Halley for the production of the *Principia*. Not only did he furnish the means for its prompt issuance, but he was the intermediary between Newton and the Society and others and the wise counsellor of all the many temperamental persons involved in its publication. In fact, had it not been for Halley there might never have been a *Principia,* and Newton might now be known primarily as an important experimenter in the field of optics and not as one of the two or three great scientists of all time.

Trinity College, Cambridge, was the last place on earth to which one would have sent a boy in the seventeenth century for training in experimental philosophy, though it was an excellent place for one seeking holy orders. Newton was sent there only because his mother's brother, the Reverend Ayscough, was a Trinity man. But Newton needed no teachers in science—he could profit most from the absence of tutors and taskmasters. Trinity College fortunately gave him what he needed most—hospitality, freedom, and a friendly spirit. Most colleges of Oxford and Cambridge would have considered him an intolerable nuisance. The vile smells that arose from his alchemy, the noise and confusion he created with his hammers and files and chisels, and his mutilation of college property by the drilling of holes and driving of nails would have made him an unwelcome guest.

Cambridge not only tolerated Newton, but it gave him in Professor Isaac Barrow a friend and advisor and promoter of priceless value. Cambridge became, therefore, "the birthplace of Newton's genius, her teachers fostered his earliest studies, her institutions sustained his mightiest efforts," her spirit of freedom and the lack of all mechanical control strengthened the independence and resourcefulness his early life had cultivated, and within her precincts were all his discoveries made that were made. He created of Trinity College a temple wherein his spirit still broods, and he quickened its college halls and its walls of stone with immortal life.

Newton considered himself primarily an experimental philosopher. His work on the composition of white light and the design of a reflecting telescope he placed first in his interest. The epoch-making discoveries in mathematics and in analysis with which his notebooks were filled, he seems to have regarded as of secondary or even of trivial interest. When his discoveries on the spectrum brought him into violent controversy with Linus and Lucas of Holland, he became so disgusted with science that he nearly quit philosophy. He longed to enter the study of law and was only saved to science by Professor Barrow, who decided in favor of his competitor when Newton applied for a fellowship in law. Thus the world owes another debt to the wise Professor Barrow for his understanding of the real Newton. Barrow was an eminent mathematician and a tutor worthy of the youthful Newton. He had wisdom enough to tolerate if not to encourage his brilliant disciple in his immortal excursions into experimental philosophy.

In 1666, during a period when Cambridge University was dismissed because of the Black Death, Newton took refuge at the family farm at Woolsthorpe. It was there that the apple is said to have fallen. In any case it was at this time that he began to speculate about gravity. But in testing out his theory of universal gravity he laid aside his computation of the moon's motion, because, as is usually stated, the then accepted radius of the earth was five hundred miles too short, and hence his calculations would not check properly against the known motion of the moon. Newton had plenty of other things to do. He was more than busy in his workshop or "elaboratory." He was as much enamored with the "universal elixir" as with "universal gravity." He was grinding lenses, observing comets, playing with alchemy, and making his discoveries on the composition of white light and the properties of the spectrum.

Not until 1684 did Newton relinquish his alchemy and return once more to his gravitational studies. In the meantime Picard had shown that the earth's radius was about 3,960 miles and not 3,450, the value taken by Newton. After using this new value to correct his former computation, Newton wrote: "The moon appears to be kept in her orbit purely by the power of gravity." According to Cajori the delay in verifying the law of universal gravitation may have been due to Newton's difficulty in solving the problem of the mutual attraction of two uniform spheres, a problem he did not solve until the summer of 1685. Then his real job began. The years 1685, 1686, and the early part of 1687 will ever be memorable in the history of science, for it was then that the *Principia* was composed and given to the world.

Every age seems to have a fundamental problem to

challenge its scholars. This is the age of the Michelson-Morley experiment. The challenge of this unsolved problem has produced more good electrodynamics and more good mathematics than have thousands of successful investigations. The Michelson-Morley dilemma of Newton's day was the problem of the moon's motion; for more than a century after his time it was the challenge that called to the contest the great men of the day—Clairaut, MacClaurin, Alembert, Euler, Lagrange, Laplace—and developed them in their strength. In Newton's day the problem had a most practical appeal. If the complex course and the irregular motions of the moon could be brought under a system of causes, then accurate tables could be computed and the position of a ship at sea could be determined. It seemed hopeless to perfect a timepiece that would keep good enough time through long sea voyages to enable the mariner to determine his longitude. By the tables of the moon of Newton's day longitude could not be determined within thirty minutes. Some five of the irregularities in the moon's motion had been discovered, but no cause was known. Galileo had explained the libration in latitude, and now Newton explained the libration in longitude. But why should the moon's speed vary in its quadrants? What effect should the changing distance from the sun have on these quadrantal speeds? Why should the perigee continuously advance? Does the moon's orbit change shape as the earth passes from the near to the far position from the sun? Does the plane of the moon's orbit rock back and forth as the earth carries it about its own annual course? What effect has the oblateness of the earth upon the motion of the moon? These and many other questions coursed through Newton's brain as he contemplated the problem of the heavens. If the principle of universal gravitation could explain and tie together all these movements and all the irregularities of movement, then there was hope that accurate tables of the moon could be prepared, that the seas could be safely navigated, and that a truly great service would be rendered humanity. The plea of the "practical" was strong with Newton as it was with many other great scientists. "Practical" is a very poor and much abused word; to Newton the determination of longitude at sea meant safe journeys, and the stimulation of intercourse, and the spread of civilization among the races of men. The "practical" often implies more altruism than the thoughtless are willing to admit.

Newton was able to give in the lunar theory of the *Principia* a fairly complete explanation of the variation, the parallactic inequality, the annual equation, the retrogradation of the nodes, the progression of the line of apsides, the evection or variation in eccentricity, and the variation in the inclination; and in an unpublished manuscript he accounted for the motion of the perigee. No progress was made toward explaining the secular acceleration for a century, until the time of Laplace and later.

The *Principia* must be viewed, therefore, not as a mere book of science, but as an epic whose story is the sufficiency of the laws of mechanics and the principle of universal gravitation to explain the motions

and all the irregularities of those motions in the phenomena of the heavens. It is the most profound story
ever put forth by human genius. The first two books
of the *Principia*, if translated from their geometrical
form into the language and symbolism of twentieth-
century analysis, could hardly be distinguished from
a modern textbook on the dynamics of a particle, so
little have two centuries added to the work of the
master. As one enters the last part of the treatise, he is
amazed at the uncanny intuition revealed in the treatment of almost every topic. The fundamental problem
of the mutual attraction of two uniform spheres, the
motions of the planets about the central sun, the motions of the four satellites of Jupiter and of the moons
of Saturn, are brought into the orderly march of the
epic. The climax of the story is reached in the analysis
of the complex motions of the moon. Next, by a re-
working of some of the material of the lunar theory,
the phenomena of the tides are explained, and, by the
very ingenious device of considering the belt of excess
material in the earth's equatorial zone as a continuous
set of moons attached to a spherical earth, the preces-
sion of the equinoxes is accounted for. Throughout
all these many chapters of the story it is gravity, with
its law of inverse squares, that is the overmastering
fate sweeping all the events to their appointed destiny.
Never had the human intellect reached so noble a conception of the nature of things.

Newton worked at the composition of the *Principia*
with an enthusiasm and a speed that was little short
of fanatical. From Humphrey Newton, whom he em-

ployed as his secretary from 1683 to 1689, to copy papers and prepare matter for the printer, etc., we know much about his personal habits. Humphrey says: "I cannot say I ever saw him laugh but once . . . his carriage was meek and humble . . . I never knew him to take any recreation or pastime either in riding out to take the air, walking, bowling or any other exercise whatever, thinking all hours lost not spent on his studies—so intent, so serious upon his studies that he ate very sparingly, nay oftentimes not at all, so that going to his chamber I have found his meal untouched, of which when I reminded him, he would reply 'Have I?' and then making to the table would eat a bite or two standing, for I cannot say I ever saw him sit at a table by himself . . . he very rarely went to bed until two or three of the clock, sometimes not until five or six, lying about four or five hours—he very seldom went to Chapel, that being the time he chiefly took his repose, as for the afternoon, his earnest and indefatigable studies retained him, so that he scarcely knew the house of prayer . . . in his chamber he walked so much you might have thought him to be educated in Athens among the peripatetic sect . . . when he has sometimes taken a turn or two he might make a sudden stand, turn himself about, run like another Archimedes with an Eureka, fall to write on his desk standing . . . his behavior was mild and meek, without anger, peevishness or passion, so free from that, you might take him for a stoic."

As we have said, the *Principia* was issued by the Royal Society about midsummer of 1687, the funds for its printing having been furnished by Halley, though the Society had originally promised to bear the expense. This great work, as might have been expected, excited a warm interest in all parts of Europe. By 1691 scarcely a copy could be secured, and a new edition was already contemplated. While it is probable that not more than twenty people in England could understand it, it nevertheless became the subject of parlor conversation and won great fame for its author. The universities, however, were at first little influenced by the new system. The Scottish universities, St. Andrews and Edinburgh, were the first to teach the philosophy of the *Principia*. Oxford, with characteristic conservatism, continued to teach the vortex theory of Descartes for many years. Even Cambridge can hardly claim to have been an early supporter of the *Principia*. While Newton was at Cambridge, he had practically no hearers at all; often not a single person showed up at his lectures. When he left Cambridge in 1696 the *Physics of Rohault* was still in use as a textbook, but fortunately it was Clark's Latin translation of the French text, which contained copious notes in which the ingenious translator explained, without bias or controversy, the views of Newton on the principal objects of discussion, so that they were virtually a refutation of the text. The student, naturally inclined to radicalism, would look into the notes and of course contend for that view. Hence we may say that the Newtonian philosophy first entered Cambridge surreptitiously and under the protection of the Cartesian philosophy.

It has never been claimed that the *Principia* is easy reading. There is a sense of unnaturalness about it that a modern student finds difficult to cast off. In reading Archimedes' works, for example, the student is conscious of no artificiality; it is like the geometrical reasoning with which he is already familiar in more elementary form. But the processes and the symbolism of theoretical mechanics are now so familiar to the reader that he finds it hard to follow reasoning without the use of the formulas and the methods of modern elementary analysis. Moreover, there is a serious incompleteness because of the fact that Newton possessed no concept of "energy" or of "mechanical work," concepts which are now fundamental in even the most elementary treatment of mechanics. Then again, those geometrical ratios so contantly occurring in the *Principia* are, as the reader knows, only trigonometric functions in disguise, and he must restrain himself from passing over from the letterpress to the methods and processes of the calculus. Of course Newton had used his method of fluxions in discovering the truth of theorems, but almost no vestige of the analytical process of discovery can be discerned in the text. As a matter of fact, the word "fluxion" does not appear anywhere in the book except in one lemma where he seems to have forgotten to change over from the analytical process of discovery into the usual synthetic form of presentation. The eleven lemmas of Section I, Book I, on prime and ultimate ratios represent material intimately associated with Newton's theory of fluxions, but it is hardly correct to regard these lemmas as introductory to the general methods of the calculus. They could quite as well appear independently in the *Principia,* even if Newton had never discovered his general theory of fluxions and fluents. In the famous lemma to Theorem V, Book II, he actually presents the rules for the fluxions of products and powers without using the term or its usual notation. In a scholium he refers to a letter to Collins of 1672 and to the then unpublished account of his method prepared in 1671.

There are two *Principias.* One is the formal *Principia* made up of the definitions and theorems in conventional and impersonal form; the other is the informal *Principia* made up of the numerous and rather extended scholia liberally scattered throughout the work, to which should be added most of the matter of the third book. It is in these informal remarks and discussions that we are able to get a glimpse of the scientific personality of Newton. Here we begin to see him as the natural philosopher and as an experimental and inventive genius. The *Principia* is a treatise on theoretical and experimental physics built up in numerous strata from the contrasting departments —hard impersonal layers of mathematics interspersed with more pliant and unconventional layers of informal discussion and common sense tabulations and observations. It was this second *Principia* that seemed to be nearest to Newton's heart. His constant appeal was to nature itself. *Hypotheses non fingo!* ("I do not form hypotheses"), he said, and added in explanation: "We are certainly not to relinquish the evidence of experiments for the sake of dreams and vain fictions of our own devising; nor are we to recede from the analogy of Nature, which is wont to be simple and always consistent with itself." "I have laid down," he says, "the principles . . . not philosophical but mathematical. These principles . . . lest they should have appeared of themselves dry and barren, I have illustrated here and there with some philosophical scholia, giving an account of such things as are of more general nature on which philosophy seems chiefly to be founded."

What is the most profound concept in the *Principia*? Perhaps it is the observation that the quantity of matter is always proportional to weight—or, as we now say, that gravitational mass and inertial mass are identical. Two centuries were required to bring out the full meaning of this fact in the theory of relativity. Newton was engrossed in its philosophical significance and in the apparent simplicity of the structure of the universe which it implies. He approached the proposition from every angle: the outer shell of a body does not insulate its interior from external gravity; changing the shape of a body does not change its total gravity at remote distances. He even contrasts these facts with magnetic action, for he says: "The power of gravity is of a different nature from the power of magnetism; for the magnetic attraction does not vary alone with the quantity of matter" but depends as well upon the kind of substance acted upon.

Genius cannot be defined, much less explained. That glover's son of Stratford-on-Avon was not selected by heredity nor by the training of schoolmen to become the poet of the ages. And there was nothing in the blood of the simple farmer folk of Woolsthorpe, Lincolnshire, and little in the discipline of Trinity College, Cambridge, that could fashion a creater of modern science. The world and heredity may have rough-hewn these characters, but we must conclude that it was a divinity, above and outside of them, that shaped their ends. We can do no better, therefore, than to say with the Greeks that genius is the gift of Zeus. His servants Melpomene and Thalia ministered unto Shakespeare, and his handmaid Urania ministered abundantly unto Newton. This is as good an explanation as the biologists or others have been able to give us. In reckoning the total riches of mankind we hardly know what part to credit to the labor of the sweating multitude and what part to credit to the dispensation of Zeus. As for the world, it merely accepts or rejects a genius and uses or abuses his great gifts. Gratitude is not one of man's conspicuous qualities. The bounty of nature, the riches arising from the work of the many, and the great gifts brought to him by genius, he is apt to accept as his by natural right, and only coldly and formally to acknowledge them in an occasional perfunctory hymn of praise.

This year (1937) is the two hundred and fiftieth anniversary of the publication of the *Principia*. On the day of its issue in July, 1687, there began a new stepping up of the power of intellect over nature and a remaking of the ancient world into a modern world. Emerson defines a great man as one who administers a shock to the world, and he names Newton as one who did that. If recent industrialism is a blessing, give initial credit to the *Principia.* If industrialism means that an end-point has been fixed for the happy life on earth, place the blame on the *Principia;* for the book is the primer of man's effort to understand and predict and control natural phenomena for his own good or to his own undoing, just as his moral powers happen to determine. Newton drew up the Magna Charta of man's power over his environment. But the *Principia* is a failure if, man's power and the unity of existence once having been revealed, it finally comes about that the intellect is insufficient to discern and control the vectors and the orbits and the tides of action at work in the daily affairs of men. After the *Principia,* man can no longer ascribe his failures or his successes to the work of demons, or to the acts of fairies, or to superstitions, or to chance, or to the perils of the age, or to the intervention of the gods. The *Principia* has placed man at the center of his own universe. The frame of reference for all social phenomena is fixed with man as origin, and nothing external offers enlargement or escape.

We no longer debate whether art or science has the greater meaning for the advancement of humanity. But there is a difference, we should note, in the way in which these two universals enter the *scheme of civilization.* Of the two, art is the more permanent, being limited only by the endurance of marble and clay and metals, and of paint and paper and canvas. If a marble of Phidias should now be unearthed it would still charm us with the beauty once given to it by the artist, just as the marbles and bronzes and papyri and tablets of Egypt and Mesopotamia still reveal the inspirations of an ancient age. But with the works of science the story is different. The discoveries of Archimedes and Newton have joined the ever growing stream of scientific truth and for the most part are dissolved in that river, unrecognized and unlabeled. They have become a part of a greater whole. Art builds up the spiritual continents, majestic and eternal. Science forms the rivers flowing on into the final ocean of reality, where each contribution blends and becomes lost amid all the others. Aeschylus and Shakespeare built mountain ranges; Archimedes and Newton started rivers at their source. Therefore, in commemorating this anniversary, we must remember that much of the *Principia* is now to be found in the contributions of many men of sagacity into whose treatises the material has threaded its way. The greatness of the *Principia* has not vanished; merely its details are becoming a shadowy though cherished memory.

The *Principia* is a good book for occasional reference for the teacher of theoretical mechanics, especially for the teacher who has a good deal of confidence in his own ability. He can quickly recover his modesty if he will but turn to the very incomplete first theory of the tides, or even to the motion of a body in a resisting medium, which he has probably been teaching his class. The uncanny genius of Newton appears in almost every topic. Take the simple problem of the rising and falling body in a medium resisting as the square of the velocity. The college junior solves this problem as a matter of routine, the details for the rising body coming out in terms of circular functions and those for the falling body in terms of hyperbolic functions. Turn now to Proposition VIII of the second book. There he will find a circle and a rectangular hyperbola whose semi-axes he can take as the terminal velocity of the falling body. Two associated points, t and T, on the circle and hyperbola are shown. The times of ascent and descent are proportional to the sectors of the circle and hyperbola respectively. The velocities at corresponding positions are laid off on the common tangent. There the whole solution is constructed geometrically, so that any velocity of projection leads immediately by plane geometry to the final velocity at the level of the ground. No circular and no hyperbolic functions are directly in evidence, but the problem is fully solved in geometrical terms which actually anticipated both of them.

The *Principia* possesses the contradictory power of either augmenting the self-confidence of the elementary student or of reducing to zero the ego of the doctor of philosophy. If the modern scientist wishes to liquidate his mathematical arrogance, let him turn frequently to the pages of the *Principia*. For example, in the case of the famous scholium on streamlined bodies, let the reader supply the proof, not given in the *Principia*, in terms of the mathematics of Newton's day. The present emphasis on problems of streamlining has again directed interest to Newton's mathematical and experimental investigation of the resistance of a moving body in a medium. In his scholium on the streamlined body, Newton said: "I conceive that this proposition may be of use to builders of ships." After two hundred and fifty years, modern automotive engineering has taken the lead and made the public streamline-conscious. Even salesmanship has helped itself to the problem and given us streamlined household devices, from cook stoves to refrigerators, and even streamlined children's toys. Mathematicians also have been attracted to this part of Newton's work as one of the first serious problems set up and solved in what would now be called the calculus of variations. A thoughtful scientist has remarked to me that the problem is a fine example of Newton's scientific courage, for, after showing that a sphere is subject to but half the resistance of a cylinder of like dimensions, he had the boldness to attack the problem of the body of *least* resistance. There existed no analogies and no evidence that this type of problem even lay in a realm susceptible of study by mathematics. No better proof of his genius can be submitted than the fearlessness with which he entered such umbral and unexplored regions.

♪

NEWTON was born on Christmas Day, 1642, a premature and weak infant that was hardly expected to survive a few hours. But that frail infant, so small that, according to his mother, he could have been placed in a quart measure, lived to the ripe age of eighty-five.

In 1696 he had been appointed warden of the mint and in 1699 master of the mint at a salary of fifteen hundred pounds, the equivalent of about thirty-five thousand dollars at the present time. This meant, of course, that Newton moved to London, where he maintained quite an establishment with six servants and a coach befitting his rank. His home was presided over by a niece, a young woman of wit, beauty, and accomplishments, Catherine Barton. She was a famous beauty of her time, and her charm and gaiety called forth the praise of the poets and the adoration of a train of suitors. It was no trouble to Newton, therefore, to entertain the best company in London at his establishment. Thus for the last thirty years of his life he practically ceased to contribute to philosophy.

He was past eighty when he began to suffer seriously from the torments of age. He had moved from Chelsea to Kensington to ease his infirmities, and there on March 20, 1727, he passed away. On Tuesday, March 28, his body was borne to Westminster Abbey and buried near the entrance to the choir on the left side. At that place has been erected a monument to him who, of all those of the Abbey, least needs a monument, and thereon, in well-poised Latin words, is the eulogy to him who least needs praise: "Who by a vigor of mind almost divine, the motions and figures of planets, the paths of comets, and the tides of the seas, first demonstrated."

Hypotheses non fingo!

THE MEANING OF SCIENCE

But we know nothing really; for truth lies deep down.—DEMOCRITUS

There is something in this more than natural, if philosophy could find it out.—SHAKESPEARE

V

Science and Reality

EVER since the days of the Greeks we have known that the approach to reality is not through the senses alone, however real sense perception may seem to us. The world brought to the threshold of our senses seems indeed a very real world, but even in our infancy we face some rude contradictions. It seems absurd, for example, that we cannot reach and touch the moon as well as reach and touch our rattle. It is fortunate that we begin life by crying for the unattainable and learning that our powers of apprehension are limited. But later we study theoretical mechanics and there learn how to reach and touch the moon by the arm of reason, and how to reach and touch many of the other early unattainables. So to become grownups and not remain mere infants, we learn the technique of a dual approach to reality—the approach through the senses and the approach through the power of reasoning.

Science, they say, depends upon measurement and hence all the ideas in the world of science are derived from the world of sense perception. Nevertheless, as Max Planck has remarked, common sense alone is not sufficient; there is a place for reason, and not only a place, but a position of supreme control. To illustrate, I ask you to think of an imaginary scientist who spends all his daylight hours in his laboratory with his instruments of brass and glass and all manner of gadgets, making and recording a multitude of observations. At night, let us suppose, this same scientist spends his hours in his study, mathematizing in the midst of his manuscripts and books—studying and thinking in terms of the postulates and symbols of mathematics. Let us suppose that the scientist continues indefinitely: day after day observing in his laboratory, and night after night mathematizing in his study. Suddenly it dawns upon him that there is a correspondence between the observations of the day and the mathematical meditations of the night; more than that, he discovers that the mathematizing of the night fills in great gaps in the experiences of the day; more than that, he finds that the studies of the night extrapolate or add truth onto the end of the facts of the day; more than that, he finds that meaning and consistency and system and an esthetic and satisfying living unity are given to the drudgeries of the day by the mathematical ecstasies of the night. Now let us ask at what time the scientist is in closest approach to the world of reality—when recording and averaging the imperfect readings of the instruments of the day or when dreaming the mathematical visions of the night? The answer to this question is the test of mathematics. Nevertheless, sooner or later, after years or it may be after many generations, it is inevitable that the mathematics of the night will no longer check and coordinate the observations of the day. This marks the beginning of a new epoch in science, for only as contradictions and paradoxes arise are the current postulates and devices of mathematics subjected to the revisions and generalizations and extensions that a new view of truth requires. To finite minds these periods of revolution must recur often and be repeated again and again. Sufficient only unto the day are the mathematics thereof. Paradoxes and contradictions are to the scientist the foundations upon which he plans and structures new truth.

A scientist should be the humblest of men. He soon learns that he dwells not in a world of reality but in a make-believe world. Reality is forever beyond him. He moves slowly toward it, but it ever eludes him. As Max Planck has said, we are compelled to contemplate the nature of things through spectacles of whose optical properties we are entirely ignorant and whose elements of design must ever remain unknown to us.

But though science is by its very nature an artificially built-up and make-believe world, this does not mean that it does not direct our gaze toward truth and reality, and of course it does not mean that mathematics is not the most potent guide to that end.

What is the nature of this guide that we call mathematics? There is no need to define it, for all creatures higher than the brutes are born mathematicians. People mathematize constantly. All games that we play are examples of mathematics. Even golf is mathematics, although not, we admit, pure mathematics, for to the definitions and postulates and conventions of golf have been added many personal and materialistic and profane attributes that have no place in science. A better illustration is the game of contract bridge. This is a two-dimensional set-up, North and South, East and West. It is played with fifty-two symbols in four so-called suits, and among the postulates is one that spades are greater than hearts, and diamonds greater than clubs, and so forth; and among the conventions is the one that West follows South in order of play—in clockwise rotation. Of course, it need not be played with material symbols nor by material players. It can be perfectly symbolized in print in a corner of the Sunday Supplement and all its orderly processes described for the reader. You may object to calling bridge a clear example of mathematics because of all the uncertainties that are involved. But these uncertainties only mean that it is a richer sort of mathematics than that of the elementary schoolbook type. After all, there is less uncertainty than you think. I always know, for example, that my partner will make the very worst play possible—there is no uncertainty about that.

But there is one real objection to my illustration: mathematics, like all science, must be productive and creative, and the game of bridge is set up to be the same day after day and night after night. We are not even permitted to say that tonight we will play in reverse order and that East shall follow South, and so on; nor that on this particular occasion the Queen shall be greater than the King, though the simplest concession to gallantry requires it, and we can prove that nothing new would result from this commutation.

Bridge is not truly mathematics until it is made the subject of a doctor's thesis. This appears to be the infallible test of science. Such an opportunity can readily be provided, however. For a thesis, let the student study the domain of a *three-dimensional* game of bridge played by six players, North and South, East and West, Up and Down, with a pack of seventy-eight cards in six suits, three red and three black, and the order of play, for example, South, Up, West, North, Down, East. You object at once that there are physical difficulties in arranging the table and players, especially the Up and Down players, to fit into the system. But all these difficulties have nothing to do with mathematics, which has no concern with matters of physical support or of materialism in any form nor, in this case, with the difficulties brought about by the force of gravity. It is merely required that the three-dimensional game be completely and adequately symbolized in the thesis and that every play and score conform accurately to the conventions and postulates set forth on page one of that thesis.

The proposed thesis illustrates the paradox that all games are mathematics but mathematics is not a game. It is necessary to emphasize the essentially expansive and constructive and creative and ungamelike character of mathematics. Mathematics never ceases to generalize and enlarge its processes. The writer of the doctor's thesis on the three-dimensional game of bridge will later in life undoubtedly write a paper for a mathematical journal on the game of contract bridge of n dimensions, played by $2n$ players with a pack of

$26n$ cards divided into $2n$ suits of 13 cards each, n black and n red. Also, if he is truly industrious, he will one day win the Nobel Prize in mathematics for his ingenious exposition of the game of bridge of an infinite number of dimensions played by a doubly infinite number of players with a pack of cards of an equal number of suits. For this game, he will probably postulate and set forth a rate of play so dense that a game may be finished in a finite time, less than a number of seconds itself less than E, and the players and card tables defined so comfortably small that the locus of each game occupies only a single molecular cubicle in the space of the mathematician's imagination.

One of the most serious afflictions of the human race is the inborn and violently hereditary deformity of right-handedness. I do not mean right-handedness in the trivial sense that a man reaches with his right arm for food and drink, but that monstrous form of right-handedness by which man reaches for conclusions with the right arm of prejudice. He has developed the long and over-muscled right arm of prejudice, apparently to become his main help in time of trouble, and has constantly exercised it to his undoing. He still possesses, after ages of experience, only a short and underdeveloped and underexercised left arm of reason, which nature intended to be the chief implement with which to reach for conclusions. I judge from conditions in Europe at the present moment that humanity is at this hour as strongly right-handed as ever. Conclusions are mostly reached by the long arm of prejudice. Woe to Europe and woe to all of us if we do not remember that it is written: "If thy right hand offend thee, cut it off!"

The left arm of reason is constructive and peaceful; the right arm of prejudice is destructive and combative. This places responsibilities on all teachers of mathematics. Here, in mathematics, is the one domain, the one insulated island of refuge, where the left arm of reason can be freely exercised and developed. Here youth can at least learn that there exist domains of truth in which prejudice and destruction have no place. How important it is, then, that all youth be made familiar with this domain. Especially should elementary geometry be studied and mastered by all. It is no accident that for centuries Euclid has been studied by the residents of the Inns of Court who expect to be called to the British bar. Geometry at least shows to youth that there is one region where the left arm of reason is powerful and where his muscles and his reach can be tested and synchronized. He will appraise the devastations of prejudice better if for a time he has dwelt where it is nonexistent.

In my lifetime there have been two developments in the power and authority of mathematics that are important enough to be called characteristics of the age in which we live. One of these is the amazing fact that all natural science has become mathematical, so rapidly, in fact, that for the first time we are taken back to the doctrine of Pythagoras, who made the first outspoken claim for the place that abstract thought must hold in solving the mysteries of phenomena. Pythagoras was a super-genius. He saw that the comprehension of the world about him was to be sought in the revelation given by mathematics. In an outburst of intuition he proclaimed that "the nature of things consists in number." In the present age, for the first time, this marvelous dictum is fully realized. The answer to any question in any science is now simply a number. It is no longer even the red or blue qualitative test of acidity of the litmus paper—it is the "hydrogen-ion concentration" expressed as a number. We can paraphrase the words of Blake, "Go deep enough, there is music everywhere," and say, "Go deep enough, there is mathematics everywhere." The various natural sciences have become mere phases of mathematics. Physics is the clanking, noisy part of mathematics; chemistry is the smelly part of mathematics; biology is the mussy part of mathematics.

Along with the development just described there has been another important change, namely, that elementary mathematical instruction has been made optional and elective. This last tendency is playing havoc with sound education and is in direct contradiction to the needs of the age. It contributes to the further development of the right-handedness of the race, at a time when rapidity of communication and other modern developments have added more danger and more explosives to an already over-prejudiced age. The leadership in elementary education is not sound at this point. Youth needs to dwell for a brief spell on the island where he can learn at least that his left arm of reason exists and has use. As Ambassador Bryce said, "It is the duty of the schools to reflect the spirit of the age without yielding to it." We should hold for adolescent youth at all hazards the opportunity for adventure in the use of his left arm of reason and not yield in this respect to the spirit of the age. We cannot approach reality through the reachings of prejudice.

The scientist does not claim that his is the only approach to reality. He realizes all too well that he can view reality only through spectacles whose optical properties are unknown. He is willing to admit that the poet and the mystic also command powers of vision, and indeed often view reality through spectacles whose optical properties are more perfect than his own. The scientist is all too conscious of the unknown aberrations and distortions and crossing of rays that are inherent in his spectacles. He admits that the poet often visions reality with less distortion, with less crossing of the rays, and with more direct parallelism in the lines of sight than is possible in the make-believe world of science. The scientist is aware of the artificiality of the domain in which he works—he knows that his postulates and imaginings and set-ups and changing theories are indeed just make-believe— quite as much so, in fact, as in the game of bridge. He envies the poet his more direct and often more inspired approach. "Go deep enough, there is music everywhere." This saying of Blake's goes to the root of things as no dictum of science possibly can. It is indeed hard to believe, it implies so much. It means that if we go deep enough, there is beauty everywhere; it means that if we go deep enough, there is goodness everywhere; it means that if we go deep enough, there is harmony everywhere. On the surface we see prejudice and ugliness and pain and suffering and wickedness, but Blake would say, "Go deeper, go deep enough into the nature of things and there is music everywhere." Who would deny, or at least who would wish to deny, that Blake is right; for it is indeed a vast symphony that is being scored, although only the initial dissonances have as yet been written down, and ages and ages must elapse before the opening theme is fully announced. Blake would have us believe that a Great Presence is mindful of the orbits of life; that there is always one best way and many less perfect ways, and that the Great Presence would guide and shield the orbits of life in the ways that are best and lead them nearer and nearer to a perfect purpose. These words make up the Creed of Evolution, and they hold alike for galaxies and for men. Go deep, go far into the scheme of things, and there is mathematics everywhere. Go deeper, go nearer and nearer to the core of reality, and there is music everywhere.

VI

Industrialism

IT IS only rarely nowadays that anyone writes hopefully of our own times; it is so easy to point out the shortcomings of the industrial age, and so difficult to see beyond the rapid changes of our times and measure the huge forces now at work in society. To many critics this is the age of material things; poetry, faith, the hope eternal, have quite forsaken the human heart. Such critics look upon the industrial leader and the engineer as just so much wasted material that in a better age might have gone to make a poet or an artist. I shall not attempt to explain industrialism, nor to seek an inner meaning without admitting the transient evils—to do so would be to claim that great epochs of readjustment are not periods of discomfort and even disaster to many of the species.

Since the dawn of civilization the only new forms of culture that have been developed are those which burst forth in the past century. The forces that have brought the race to its present place—at least most of them—are readily agreed upon. First is war, then religion, then poetry and literature, then art, philosophy, commerce, music, capital, politics, society, science, industrialism. The first in this list I name in the order of their force or potency. The final two—science and industrialism—I name last with prophetic intent.

They are the new giants in modern civilization, and they are novel in this, that they are the first great forms of culture that are antagonistic to some of the ancient types which have so long dominated human destiny.

Must I justify giving war first place among the forces that have created the civilization of today? It is enough to illustrate it by our own century and a third of national experience. War it was that gave us independence. It was the Mexican War that made us a Pacific as well as an Atlantic power—with all the consequences that must ultimately flow therefrom. Again, it was civil war that knit us together as a nation, and made us strong to work out our destiny as a single people. And again it was war that entered us upon our career as a world power, a new nationalism at home, a new imperialism abroad. And lastly, it was war—trivial it is true, only a Panama revolution let loose from Washington, but nevertheless war—that gave us Panama and has led to one of the most far-reaching results of all time—namely, the proof that the white man can conquer the tropics. Thus is war the mightiest, as well as the most monstrous, of the forces that have yet influenced the race.

These old forces of civilization—war, religion, poetry—have been harmonious co-workers; only occasionally has there been a rift in the happy family. Whether war for religion's sake, or religion in the cause of war; poetry in praise of war and its heroes, or poetry in the service of religion, the forces have for the most part pulled together, and their paths have converged. Homer, Achilles, Moses, David, Caesar, Mohamet, Charlemagne, Dante, Shakespeare, Napoleon, George Bernard Shaw, all are artists painting upon the same canvas.

ƒ

IN A LARGE SENSE, science and industrialism are not two forces, but a single force. Industrialism is merely science in action, or militant science. But this distinction is a large one. To make industrialism from science, one must add other elements—such as ambition for power, greed for exploitation, or lust for money, or some combination of these. Of course industrialism could not have developed except from the soil of science.

The brief history of industrialism is interesting. I shall divide it into three periods. In the beginning the exploitation of labor was, perhaps, the dominant characteristic. Now the exploitation of labor was nothing new in the world, for it dates back to the time of the first slave. What I mean is that after a long period of partial emancipation, in which the common man had won a certain right to individual assertion and independent existence, industrialism came along and built up great groups of dependent workers. The exploitation of labor was developed on a new scale and almost consciously, as in slavery.

As industrialism grew and science pointed out more and more of the real meaning of the new movement, the exploitation of labor became more nearly secondary to the exploitation of nature, or of natural resources. To take into private possession and hold against the people the natural wealth of a country was not, perhaps, an altogether new thing, but the machines, the processes, the transportation, the organization, the communication that science developed made the exploitation possible and abundantly worth while.

Next industrialism entered upon the third and greatest period, namely, the period characterized by the exploitation of the middle classes. Here is one of the important developments of our times. The so-called middle classes are almost solely the product of industrialism. The modern industries of a country and the commerce resulting therefrom are the only forces that have ever built up a large middle class. The best ways to tap the savings of this class, although just discovered, are now pretty well worked out. The American industrial trust, the German syndicate, the new-style organization of banking, the perfected method of handling investment and holding companies, the public service corporations, the modern stock exchange, these are some of the manifestations of the great vacuum cleaner that is sucking away at the savings of the middle classes. This, I say, is the richest field of exploitation yet discovered.

Do not misunderstand me, however. I do not mean that at a meeting of the directors of the Biggest National Bank, or of the Greatest Holding Company, or of the United States Industrial Corporation, the captain of the captains of industries arises and says: "Gentlemen, the exploitation of the middle classes is the greatest discovery of modern times. What can we do today to further this cause? What is next to do to tap the savings of this class?" I say I do not mean that this actually happens. A thing need not be done consciously in order to be done. The result is the same whether done consciously or unconsciously. What I mean is, for example, that a monopoly price for goods against a world market is an instance of the exploitation of the middle classes. Remember, also, that formerly the savings in the cost of production by improved methods and new inventions accrued largely to the consumer. Under modern organization of industry this saving goes very largely to increased profits and, still more, to increased capitalization—that is, it is taken from the pockets of the middle classes.

Formerly the leaders in the industries were manufacturers, men not far removed from the middle classes themselves. Today those leaders are not manufacturers, but so-called financiers, artists in the handling of funds, men interested in profits, not products—profits in large part made from the middle classes by the nursing of stocks and the shuffling of securities, and not merely by the manufacture and sale of realities. Again, the control of banks and investment companies, for the purpose of industrial adventure and for strategic ends, works primarily against the middle classes. The irony in the situation, which makes the cleaning-up process almost perfect, is that it is the middle classes themselves upon whom are unloaded, through organized underwriting campaigns and the short-circuiting of the market, the very obligations created in the organization of the exploiting machinery.

There are many other counts that might be added to the true bill against industrialism. Many of these are brought to our attention by those who dote on the apparent shortcomings of the present era. Industrialism has fostered city life, and has put the moral and physical fibers of men to new tests. It has attracted the brightest intellects to leadership in its army, much to the loss of politics and the professions and the arts. All these things are in a way true. It is not, however, the purpose of this paper to convict industrialism, but to acquit it, so I must not enlarge upon its apparent shortcomings. I shall now attempt to show that industrialism, moving forward on the rails laid by science, is working for good and not for evil, and that the features commonly criticized are only transient phases of a great movement which, in its main features, is making for the advance of the race toward the highest ideals.

Let me again remind you that industrialism is merely another name for science in action. The pure science of the study or laboratory it is not. But this same pure science joined to some form of worldly ambition is industrialism. Therefore, where science leads it must follow. It is, I claim, the most dependent upon science of all purely worldly activities. Trace forward what science must do for us, and we shall comprehend whither industrialism is leading.

Do not forget these truths: It is science that is dominating this age, this twentieth century, and not industrialism. Science works through industrialism. Science dominates industrialism. Science corrects the evils it itself creates. Science has not only changed the forms and the conditions of our physical existence, it has altered our mental life, has controlled our views and changed the basis upon which rest our fears, hopes, and opinions. The old forms of culture have been so long present in the life of the race that it is hopeless to attempt to trace out their contribution to society. Causes have slowly fused with effects, and influences at first external have become internal, a part of life itself. Not so with the newest type of culture. Science is now at work remaking the world, primarily a force from without. Its first effect is spiritual rather than material. It has spread through humanity a spirit of optimism. It has made optimists of everyone, especially of the common man. So much has been accomplished by science, even though it is but vaguely comprehended, that the ordinary man deems all things possible. Science, through its many phases and effects, has become the moral sunshine of modern life. It warms and cheers and gives a joy and a hope to this present life that former generations hesitatingly attributed only to a future existence.

I shall now illustrate the way in which science corrects the evils it itself creates, and show that the dangers brought in by the new culture are merely transient. Science, the father of industrialism, is the ultimate parent of that tremendous exploitation of the natural wealth of the world which in two generations has spent more of our coal, iron, and many other re-

sources than were used by all the preceding generations. Science has created the problem of conservation.
Now I read nowhere in the books of the conservation-
ists that science is the real criminal that has caused
our natural resources to be exploited. Perhaps I do
not find it there because science, now the prosecutor,
must forget its own crimes.

Science has not only created the problem of conservation, but it has spread abroad a spirit of optimism
that makes men believe that all will still be well when
the soil is in the ocean, and iron is rust, and the last
lump of coal is on the hearth. It is science that has
created the new faith that makes conservation so difficult a problem. But if science has created the problem
of conservation and has spread a faith that is an obstacle to its solution, it is still true that science alone
can furnish the remedy. It is but poetic justice that
science and its leaders must now point the way and
carry much of the burden. Science must now give, and
it is giving, the solution of the problem it has itself
created.

What is true of the problem of conservation is true
of all of the difficulties and evils brought to us by
science, whether directly or through industrialism.
Science brings its own remedies and removes the evils
that it has itself created. If it were otherwise, science
would not be science.

A second effect of industrialism, one that is rarely
credited to it, is the changed view of the prosperous
classes with respect to their obligation to society in
general. Public opinion no longer supports the man

who gives no form of high service to his fellow men. The very fact that business and industry are organized on so large a scale must convince us that the personal independence of the proprietor no longer exists. Scores of new checks and dependencies hedge him about. He sees that his life must be one of social purpose. As obscurely as this truth is often seen, and as glaringly as it is contradicted by the sporty spirit and the social itchings of the newly rich, we must hold it to be one of the characteristics of our era that it is social purpose and not play that is dignified by industrialism. Riding to hounds as a vocation no longer gives the social satisfaction it once did.

Let us now turn from these, which are after all minor effects of industrialism, to a consideration of some of its major tendencies. Perhaps the greatest contribution of science and industrialism to our era is the removal of controversy from human progress. This is indeed a great service to mankind—to narrow the field of strife, to remove obstacles, to settle public matters by bringing to bear accurate data, adequate analysis of cause and effect, and expert judgment, so that contention and partisanship and politics tend to be eliminated and questions settled on their own merits. This trait of the industrial age is fast developing. The numerous expert commissions appointed by the states and by the federal government to investigate and determine important questions upon the basis of exact knowledge are a pertinent illustration. These matters should never again become the football of partisanship or political manipulation. Likewise the commission form of municipal government is removing from the field of politics and of local contention many questions which are really largely matters for skill and exact science. The best kind of water supply, the proper sort of sewage disposal, the best way to handle streets, street railways, public parks, schools, playgrounds, public health, the housing problem, and so on, are no longer matters settled by fight or ballot in well-ordered communities. There is always a best way, and experts are selected to find and direct it. The modern civilized community is no longer a state, but a school. The body politic has become one vast, complexly organized research institution. Governments, in this age of industrialism, should be the instruments for replacing darkness with light, for substituting for the indefinite and approximate the definite and accurate. This is about all there is to the best public service. The state must become a thinking, investigating organization, or laboratory, or research institution. There is this distinction, however, between the school and the state: the school researches only, the state researches and acts.

The illumination of public matters by modern scholarship is illustrated by what is constantly occurring in the countries of western Europe. There, as everyone knows, municipalities are in the hands of experts whose life work is a study, as in a laboratory, of the needs of the community and its individuals. Nothing is left to chance, and little to choice, except when the people can be trusted to choose wisely. The city and the state with their utilities, sanitary inspection, land purchase, construction and sale of homes for working men, control of food, care of children, supply of milk, expert advice to mothers, all sorts of special schools, museums, galleries, theaters, concert halls, municipal banks, pawnshops, employment bureaus, industrial insurance, old-age pensions, etc., etc., are conducting a laboratory for racial and civic betterment, and are carrying upon their broad shoulders the burden that a democracy would shift to the people themselves. All new or difficult questions receive special study, and an honest attempt is made to settle them in the best manner.

Another of the major influences of industrialism has been its destructive power over democratic government. Democracy, the dream of the eighteenth century, became the illusion of the nineteenth. Government of the people, by the people, has not only never been realized, it would probably have been undesirable had it been realizable. Whatever name may be given to the modern well-ordered government, it is not democracy. The duties of the state have become too complicated, too much continuity of service and scholarship is required of its experts, to permit that direct dependency upon the electors that democracy presupposes. About as well select a university faculty by popular vote as to get together the administrative body of a great state by choice of the people. Those governments which are most democratic in form have not always been most democratic in fact. In America we have had rule by those who could profit most by ruling. Again, American democracy has been minimized by the courts of law, a new sort of autocracy little dreamed of by the makers of our government— a form of autocracy that would long ago have proved intolerable had it not been for the scholarship and patriotism of our higher courts. The popular preachers of democracy contradict, in their own policies, their doctrine that the ills of democracy can be cured by more democracy. The short ballot, the numerous commissions, and many other planks of their platform have little to do with government of the people, by the people. What is left is government for the people. There is daily less and less in government that can be left to chance and less that should be left to choice. The public welfare has become complex, controlled by the intricacies of modern organized society. Its proper guidance is a field for skill and knowledge and special training rather than for the popular vote.

The last of the major influences of industrialism that I shall consider is its effect upon Christianity. A startling phenomenon of the nineteenth century was the panicky alarm which the church showed for a time as science rather suddenly took its place among the older forces of civilization. Churchmen became especially agitated over Darwinism and the uncovering of the facts at the basis of the genesis of species. The Bishop of Oxford, in his now famous attack on Darwinism at the British Association meeting of 1860, was as little prepared for the rapidity with which his position would become obsolete among his own clergy as he was for the swiftness and completeness of Huxley's reply. For a time there was conflict and controversy. Then there followed peace. The clergy soon realized that to be a priest of darkness was to be no priest at all. The church discovered that science and scholarship were not its enemies.

Even at the present time, however, the world has not fully awakened to the fact that science, so far from being an enemy, is the most potent ally that Christianity has yet had. During the twenty centuries of its history Christianity has not struggled alone. War, poetry, art, music, have diligently served it. But it has required the slow treading of centuries for man to discover that war has no place in such a list. It seems unbelievable sometimes that the progress of great ideas should be so incredibly slow among our race. The patience of Providence is boundless, for almost without exception his truths penetrate humanity only after many centuries. And Christianity itself is no exception. In one sense Christianity may be said to have died out a generation or two after the death of Christ, for it was then that its fundamental truth began to vanish. When in the Middle Ages the church deemed itself more powerful than worldly dynasties, it had, as regards the essence of Christ's teachings, lost all but the semblance of the truth. Christianity was too profound a doctrine and humanity too frail a vessel.

The esssential and profound truth of Christianity I take to be this: that the law of the jungle, the law of the tooth and claw, must be replaced by a higher law; that humanity can reach its most perfect development and realize the highest ideals only through the reign of unselfishness. The beginning of Christianity thus marks the transition of man from the kingdom of a lower to the kingdom of a higher being. The Golden Rule is the definition that distinguishes one domain from the other. It has become the mission of the industrial age to separate out the essential doctrine of Christianity from the unessential.

That the message of Christianity is opposed to some of the primitive forces of culture, such as war, for example, has been but poorly discerned. War is the most perfect embodiment of human selfishness. It is selfishness in its most concentrated and most brutal form. Let us give credit to this industrial age that has laid bare these simple truths. Science has replaced war among the allies of Christianity. The exploration of nature has revealed and demonstrated the inadequacy of the law of the jungle for human progress. Science has supplied us with the methods and the laws wherewith to check up human phenomena and the means of showing wherein and to what extent the selfish elements are controlling human activities. Science is supplying the instruments, the test tubes and the balances, not for material things alone, but for checking up our own experiences, and for applying to life itself those tests that determine the principles which control in each configuration.

If science has given us the tools, the methods, the point of view, industrialism has given us the laboratory and the fiery furnace in which to test them. The assembling of men in great dependent groups, the subdivision of human effort, the new conditions of life, the accidents and dangers of modern industrial employment, have forced upon us problems in bulk, and not in single instances. The business world has shown us how to divide up investments, risks, and profits by the joint-stock organization. It has drilled us in the elimination of hazards and the division among the many of the ownership and rewards of industry. This very phenomenon emphasizes by contrast and makes it inevitable that society share the hazards of the life of the individual. To place the burdens of the individual upon the broad shoulders of the state is therefore but a reflex from industrialism itself. A community of interests among the prosperous classes and class hatred between the proprietary and the working classes cannot permanently coexist. If the industrial trust brings peace where there was war, this peace must finally extend to humanity itself. Industrialism has eliminated the middle ground and the possibility of compromise. Peace between the giant groups is progress; warfare between the giant groups is destruction. Science cures the ills it itself creates.

There is thus offered to our era, as the essential term of permanence, the acceptance of the fundamental message of Christianity. Unselfish cooperation, appreciation, and love of our fellow travelers is the condition of progress. The industrial age when it fully develops must become the most cultured, the most gracious, the kindliest of the eras that the human family has yet lived. Industrialism compels the rule of men by the principle of charity. It has brought us to a climax in human affairs. Charity, love, unselfishness, the Golden Rule—whatever you may name the law—has begun to be the necessary and sufficient condition of advance. This present era is not the old age of Christianity—it is its childhood. As the biologist might say, the industrial age is a period of rapid mutation. The type is changing. It is a day of hope and optimism such as the world has not hitherto known.

$\mathcal{S}$

THUS FAR TO 1912, when the above paper was first published. This is the year 1938. The optimism it reveals will now cause a smile, and the further fact that I still adhere to it will raise a laugh. But the forces let loose in society by industrialism have not yet compounded their major resultants. Unfortunately evolution is in no hurry—the results that man impatiently requires in a few weeks, nature is apt to fumble over for years or even for ages. Nature seems to possess no sense of economy of time. She devoted a hundred million years trying to make a citizen of the trilobite. From the beginning of the Cambrian age onward the trilobite was in complete possession of the earth. There were aquatic trilobites, of which some swam the open sea, others crawled upon the beach. Herbiverous trilobites lived upon the vegetation, and carniferous trilobites preyed upon them. Diminutive forms of trilobites lived in the stalks of plants and in the branches of trees to keep safe from enormous forms prowling beneath. In fact, the world was one hundred per cent trilobite-minded and no other style of life seemed socially proper. If there had been a trilobite historian looking backward over one hundred million years of trilobite existence, he would have justly concluded that the world had been expressly created for trilobites and that their possession of the earth was to be perpetual. But it all came to naught. No remnant, not even a remote descendant, of this race of creatures now inhabits the earth. Nature is prodigal of time—one hundred million years allotted to the trilobite experiment, and only a few million in all to the life of *homo sapiens*. No wonder, then, that man becomes impatient. He is, it is true, gifted with the sense of prophecy, but not with the clairvoyance necessary to foresee the exact date of eventualities. He appraises the causes at work in society and their ultimate culmination, but the time thereof, even when within his own control, seems to be checked off only on an inscrutable calendar concealed on Olympus.

I am stubborn enough to persist in the belief that industrialism has built up, and continues to build up, a society of institutions rather than a society of individuals. Individualism is giving way to institutionalism. The units of society are no longer individuals, but institutions. We have industrial corporations, labor unions, Daughters of the American Revolution, universities and colleges, American Legions, public utilities, Rotarians, churches, organized crime, chain stores, farmers' unions, consumer cooperatives, chambers of commerce, fruit-growers' associations, bank-share corporations, women's clubs, manufacturers' associations, Boy Scouts, investment trusts, peace societies, trade associations, fair practice leagues, the

American Bar Association, steel institutes, and a host of similar institutions that in large part have replaced the individual as the unit in what was formerly called democracy. This is the work of science operating through industrialism. The new rapid transport, the new communication by telephone and teletype, and many other unifying devices have converted the corporation into an elephant with a hundred trunks and transformed the labor union into an octopus of a thousand suckers. Industrialism has substituted institutionalism for individualism. It must all materialize for the general good. These giant groups can work out a tolerable destiny only by cooperation. The present state of warfare between some of them is merely a symptom of a temporary trilobite age. Warfare between the giant groups is destruction. Peace among the giant groups is progress. An optimist believes that the end of civilization is not yet. He sees that cooperation is possible in Sweden under capitalism and that the "forced cooperation" within the totalitarian states of Italy, Germany, and Russia may be only the preliminary training necessary to produce a more altruistic society. The examples from the industrial age, feeble as they may appear in the present world chaos, nevertheless seem to show that cooperation is slowly emerging as the only philosophy on which man can survive. Science cures the ills it itself creates.

VII

Science and Authority

IN a great treatise on the Chinese civilization I find the following statement by Oscar Peschel: "Since our intellectual awakening, since we Europeans have appeared on the arena of history as the creators and guardians of the treasures of culture, we have sought only one thing, of the presence of which the Chinese had no idea, and for which they would give hardly a bowl of rice. This invisible thing we call causality. We have admired a vast number of Chinese inventions, but even if we search through their huge treasures of philosophical writing, we are not indebted to them for a single theory or a single glance into the relation between cause and effect."

These words may be unjust to the civilization of China, but they certainly apply truthfully to the ancient civilizations of Babylonia and Egypt. There can be no doubt that the ultimate in human attainment was reached by the Greeks. They seem to have been God's chosen people to receive the last of the revelations; namely, that there was for all things a causality independent of fears or hopes, uninfluenced by prayers and incantations, and undisturbed by fairies, demons, or gods—the connectivity of event with event, a dependence of fact upon fact; a universe of cause and effect.

SCIENCE IN A TAVERN

Science, then, was a gift to the world from the Greeks. They were the first to proclaim the sufficiency of phenomena to explain phenomena, uncontrolled by the conduct of men or by the will of the gods. They put tradition and authority and religion into a new category and dared to point a disdainful finger at fate. In a word, it was the Greeks who made a Chinese world into a modern world. The older revelations of poetry and art and religion seemed to require the power of tradition and authority for their evolution, but this new thing that the Greeks produced required, on the contrary, the destruction of the notion of authority and demanded a reversal in the processes by means of which art and religion had developed their control over men. The beginning of science was, therefore, nothing short of a spiritual revolution. It required a declaration of independence from tradition and authority; it constituted perhaps the greatest advance the human race has ever made.

I wish to make clear that this revolution was restricted to a single field of activity. It was an intellectual revolution, a revolution in man's attitude toward phenomena and did not mean that violence must be done to the beliefs and practices of men in the domains of art and religion. Mind became a rebel, it is true, but only against man's attitude toward natural truth. The revolution made no excursion into the realms of art and ethics. The accumulated experience of the race, the national traditions, as well as the authority of the masters, still held sway over the arts and controlled the social institutions of the people.

Science was the only rebel, and the revolt did not spread to other domains. The challenge to the traditional view of natural phenomena did not lessen the rule of goodness and beauty in the regime of the world, nor did it affect the satisfactions they could give. Science did not proclaim a general but only a local revolt.

§

IN THE modern revival of natural science Bacon and Descartes merely turned us back to the original ideas of the Greeks. Bacon demanded that the first resolve of the scientist should be "to sweep away all theories and common notions, and to apply the understanding thus made fair and even to a fresh examination of particulars." Descartes put the matter in even stronger language: "Doubt," said he, "all things that can be doubted." "The man of understanding should," he claimed, "face the problems of the world himself, unprejudiced by the various and conflicting solutions of these problems which have been handed down to him from past generations. His own reason is adequate for truth, and he must seek it alone without help from unreason."

Now it is obvious that one can only partially succeed in ridding himself of traditional ideas. But the degree to which the scientist succeeds in cutting himself off from tradition and authority is the measure of his genius. This is the first point I desire to make. The second is that scientific progress, both in the race and in the individual, consists of a succession of cycles or waves, in which the rule of authority and the rule of reason each have their turn—an endless alternation of the dominance of old theory with the dominance of new thought, loyalty to and worship of the past followed by an expedition into a new future and a battle royal with tradition. Even the story of Descartes illustrates this point. His own thinking led to a new school of thought and to a new tradition, which his disciples followed with devotion and loyalty, even priding themselves on their conformance. Science may be said to advance, therefore, through the unequal pulling and hauling of the fundamentalists and the modernists of the laboratory; and the individual scientist advances only as these two conflicting moods within him tend to give a resultant that points toward progress.

Note, for example, the imperial power that the doctrines of Sir Isaac Newton held for so many generations. Everyone recognizes, of course, the greatness of Newton's name, but that does not give him a kingly position nor autocratic authority. It justifies only such rule as his sagacity can earn. Not only was his genius revolutionary, but unfortunately it was powerful enough to build up an authority that persisted for two centuries and, by a sort of dogmatism, set up and perpetuated crucial errors—not superficial errors or errors of approximation, but deep-seated errors concerned with the very nature of things. Newton's doctrine, of course, was the sufficiency of the laws of mechanics and the principle of universal gravitation to explain all the motions and all the irregularities of the motions in the phenomena of the heavens.

SCIENCE AND AUTHORITY

After two centuries Newton seemed to have made good, for the Newtonian theory entered this century with every mechanical fact in the solar system accounted for except the motion of the perihelion of Mercury. "Except the motion of the perihelion of Mercury!"—here was the rub! It took this stubborn fact and the results of the Michelson-Morley experiment to arouse the slumbering genius of scientists. The Newtonian principle had slowly been raised to the position of a dogma in an established and almost sacred school of thought. It took courage and ingenuity to show where the trouble lay: that it was the very first postulates of Newton that were wrong; that the ancient conception of space and time, as adopted by Newton, constituted a logical impediment to the explanation of the very thing set up as the universal principle—namely, gravitation. The command of Descartes to "doubt all things that can be doubted" had been forgotten. The first assumption of Newton, that a fixed frame of reference can be set up in space, was the first postulate to fall before the attack of Einstein. Then the new relativity was set up, for the most part based on principles so obvious that it seemed unbelievable that they could have been overlooked for six generations. Now we are engaged again in the process of making the general theory of relativity into a school of thought, with its converts and worshippers, awaiting the advent of a new adventurer who will be able to follow Descartes' dictum and doubt everything in the new philosophy that can be doubted. Thus we proceed in an endless alternation, each age awaiting a genius who can free the science of his time from the rule of authority.

I recall how hard we found it a few years ago to accept the thesis of Max Planck that the transfer of energy took place by discontinuous jumps and not by a continuous flow, as had been the fixed belief and tradition for a century. But at the present moment the atomic unit of energy, the quantum, is in danger of binding us to a new habit of thought quite as sterile in its consequences as the former tradition. In no field of human activity is independence and even radical individualism quite so important as in the pursuit of the natural sciences. I have often noticed that too much erudition, too much knowledge of what is in the books, may actually be a handicap to the scientist. He needs to possess a stock of ignorance large enough to lead him to dare something new, and to give him courage to strike out in a direction that the books might teach him to avoid. It is always safe to doubt many things written down in the sacred scriptures of science. It is well to doubt not only all the things that can be doubted, but also some of the things that cannot be doubted, and even a few of the things that must not be doubted.

Let us consider for a moment what application of the ideas we are here presenting can be made in individual cases, and especially how they apply to the personal needs of those who are starting out on scientific careers. Does this line of thought mean that the student of science can prepare himself for his work and at the same time ignore the accumulated literature of his subject? Does it mean that he may view lightly all the accomplishments of the past? It is certainly not my purpose to preach either of these doctrines. I am not pointing a way of escape from the necessity of commanding the literature of the subject. It is the attitude of the scientist toward this literature that matters. He must put himself in the position not of a worshipper but of a questioner and a critic of the literature. The annals of science are not books of sacred writings, but only reports of current progress; the implication is that the past is no more than a starting point for the future. To say this is not to deny to past workers in science the honor that is due them. It only describes the method by which science grows. In your desire to advance knowledge, search earnestly for a few places, a few cracks, into which you can insert wedges of doubt; do not hunt merely for the many places where you can refine and expand the claims already set forth. Discovery is somewhat explosive and is apt to disturb those who claim to be in authority. Discovery flows from the blows of questions thrust at nature. The courage to strike these blows is born of freedom from the rule of authority. In the lexicon of science "doubt" precedes "conformability."

You may claim that what I say applies to the revolutionary geniuses of science, but has no application to the beginner. It is just at this point that I would wish to make my case. The beginner in science will profit most from consciously cultivating a spirit of rational questioning and common sense doubt and by struggling constantly to free himself from the awe of authority. This is part of the training of his calling. It is of eminent use to him in the daily chores of science, and his work will be better if he can cultivate this attitude. Science cannot be built up alone through the epoch-making doubts of genius. The individual worker needs to make the spirit as well as the technique of science his own.

THE SUGGESTION that the rule of tradition in science is too potent in America at the present day does not imply that the same is true of other fields. In literature, art, and music, I am convinced that quite the opposite is the case. In these fields the rule of the established canons of taste, the force of experience, and the law of precedent and tradition all come first in importance. A questioning and radical spirit usually plays havoc with both art and music and makes them seem ridiculous. I suggest that we are suffering at the present day from the attempt of the cultivators of art to assume an irreverence toward the past that is useful only in the field of natural science. Science, I fear, has exerted a bad influence upon modern art and letters. We admit that it is not desirable to stereotype the canons of art, but only a part of the rebellious temper useful in science is needed to give a new trend and a spirit of advance to art. The attitude of science toward natural truth does not apply to those older and deeper realms to which art, poetry, and religion belong. Doubt as little as you can if you would have an understanding of beauty and of goodness.

The social sciences must be approached more conservatively than the natural sciences. The laws and customs and the social institutions and taboos of organized society have a momentum that must be diverted very cautiously. Nevertheless, it is very easy to overstress the conservative approach. We can afford to doubt much traditional economic authority and can overdo our belief in the virtue of all existing institutions.

In the natural sciences, new discoveries are quickly acknowledged and generously rewarded; the original thinker and inventor may have the protection of patents and may reap public and even financial reward. In the social sciences, on the other hand, the uncovering of new facts and principles leads to opposition and bitter criticism; "the inventive mind is more or less ostracised, and new ideas that touch upon the key problems of modern life, namely, the control of human and economic activities, are at once branded as radical and dangerous." The profound scientific discoveries of recent times are not called "communistic" or "unpatriotic," although they may be just as subversive of existing institutions as are the schemes of the Fabians. Those who years ago opposed human slavery met with opprobrium, but the scientific inventors who made slavery unprofitable, and were even the agents that destroyed it, acquired riches and power as their reward. When the control of railroad rates and pools was first proposed, it was opposed as destructive and socialistic, but when automobile-makers, by their cars and trucks, forced railroads to insolvency and robbed stockholders of their equities, no group of men was so richly rewarded.

Hence we see that in the social sciences it takes courage and unusual virility to bring the proper doubts to bear upon the existing economic practices. In the natural sciences it is part of the worker's duty to support the heroic few who attempt to drive wedges of doubt in the midst of old and traditional tenets of economic theory, for in the social sciences error puts up a vicious fight and dies hard in the field.

As the volumes of science become filled with more and more of the findings of fact and the accumulation in each narrow field tends to submerge even the activities of the specialist, the danger from the rule of authority becomes greater than ever. The difficult technique, the elaborate apparatus, the complicated organization required, make it easy to create schools of thought whose doctrines soon become dogmas and whose traditions tend to become sacred. Part of the preparation of the young scientist consists, therefore, in knowing the dangers of the scientific machine. The dictum of Descartes is now more timely than ever: "Doubt all things that can be doubted."

VIII

The Side Shows of Science

WHO can forget the glories of Barnum's Greatest Show on Earth? The press agents of that day appropriated in full paragraph 192 of Roget's *Thesaurus of English Words,* which reads: "Huge, immense, enormous, mighty, amplitudinous, stupendous, gigantic, colossal, Gargantuan"—and even then confessed to inadequacy of description. It was from these press agents that American youth learned its first lesson in the eloquence of understatement. Nevertheless, all adjectives had to be abandoned in describing the riches of the side shows. The only suitable appeal seemed to lie in huge canvases of pictorial art coupled with the oratory of the barker. To the right of the big top was the side show of the huge, to the left stood the side show of the small. Hugeness was exhibited in human form in the person of the fat woman, all parts of whose framework, such as fingers, hands, forearms, calves, and quintuple chin, each and all tended to a spherical form, so great was the pressure of calories within her. Her none too solid flesh was bulbous with pent-up vigor, forcing all parts of her epidermis to maximum volume and minimum area.

On the left of the big top stood the side show of the small, the home of the midgets General Tom

Thumb and Commodore Nutt, proclaimed by a vast painted canvas of Barnum himself displaying each of the midgets nestled in a side pocket of his coat.

At the present day the big circus seems to have come upon evil times. Perhaps the modern public is too opinionated to support so modest a show. Science has rushed in to take possession of public attention and is supplanting its rival in the patronage of the masses. The public's longing for the curious and the impossible still exists, but it is the circus of science that undertakes to satisfy it. Science, as a matter of fact, has become the Greatest Show on Earth. Its press agent is called Science Service and it sends forth daily stories of freaks and mysteries and fascinates the public with accounts of the unbelievable. Science Service counts that day lost that leaves the public with only the thrills of yesterday.

The big top of the science circus is the home of traditional science, of science of the more settled sort, where nature's laws seem to hold, and cause and effect are still operative. This is the conservative science of the good old days: Archimedes in his bathing act, Galileo on the pendulum of the flying trapeze, Laplace with his juggling spheres, Darwin with his troop of monkeys, and Marconi balancing on wireless wires. Here we find also the popularizers of science, making much noise with their brass band, but giving pleasant entertainment to the masses, although the public often wonders whether science itself can be as hard to understand as the popular exposition of it.

There is always a portion of science that is more

contradictory and more uncertain than the rest, where freaks predominate and where make-believe plays an important role. This erratic material belongs in the side shows of science and not in the more routine exhibit in the big top. Here is found science in the making, much of which will never be rational enough to warrant a place in the main show. These freakish exhibits are divided into the side show of the huge on the right and the side show of the small on the left. The fat lady of science is astronomy, for astronomy has grown big by devouring other sciences. Astronomy should not be looked upon as a science in itself; it is the fat built up from the three sciences of mathematics, physics, and chemistry in equal portions. Its devotees form a brotherhood dwelling on mountaintops, not in poverty, however, but endowed with scores of millions of dollars of shiny apparatus. One of its duties is to astound us with big numbers far beyond our power to comprehend, and to scare us with the enormous dimensions of time and distance. It fills space with countless millions of spiral nebulae of which our own galaxy is but one. It traces these out to a distance of five hundred million light-years and is now building a two-hundred-inch machine to trace them out perhaps twice as far. All this ends in confusion, for it takes so long for the light from the distant galaxies to reach us that no one can ever know where these galaxies really are or what they look like at the present moment. What we have before us is not reality but a freak universe which never did nor ever will exist. The big numbers they play with tend to bore us to death. We cannot be expected to take much interest in the huge dimensions of an expanding universe which is already much too big. I learned early in life that not everything in Barnum's side shows was one hundred per cent real. I soon suspected that the Dog Faced Man used make-up, and that the Mermaid swimming about in the glass tank was only a co-ed adorned with fins. Therefore we need not be too greatly overwhelmed with all that is shown us in the side show of the huge. Possibly some monstrosities have used make-up and perhaps part of the show is professional make-believe.

Of great interest is the side show of the small, for here from ancient days have been shown some of the most marvelous exhibits of science. Men soon learned that the small could not be built up from the large, but that the large might be built up from the small. Democritus and Lucretius proposed to search out the secrets of the small in order to understand the behavior of the large. Lucretius was the first showman to invite the public into the side show of the left. He was the greatest showman of them all, for he was the first to clothe logic with beauty and the only one to adorn common sense with the harmonies of poetry. The show of Lucretius was many-sided, but we may pick out two portions that were basic to his exhibit: First, things cannot be generated from nothing; second, there exist ultimate small things, so small that nothing can be smaller, from which alone the finite things of the world have been created and whose secrets, when understood, will prove to be all-sufficient to explain the nature of things:

SIDE SHOWS OF SCIENCE

I. Nothing from Nothing

And this first principle of her design
Shall be our starting point: nothing is ever
Begotten by divine will out of nothing.
  For if things came from nothing, every kind
Might be born out of every thing; naught then
Would require seed. Thus men might rise from ocean,
The scaly race out of the land, while birds
Might suddenly be hatched forth from the sky:
Cattle and other herds and every kind
Of wild beast, bred by no fixed law of birth,
Would inhabit tilth and wilderness alike.
No fruit would remain constant to its tree.

II. The Smallest Particles

And all those particles that congregating
In denser union, collide and rebound
Through minute intervals, being entangled
By their own close-locked shapes, these atoms
    form
The strong substance of rocks, and stubborn
    lumps
Of iron, and all other things like these.
Then of the rest a smaller number roam
All through the empty space, and as it were
In never-ending conflict waging war,
Combating and contending troop with troop
Without pause, kept in motion by perpetual
Meetings and separations; so that this
May help you imagine what it means
That the primordial particles of things
Are always tossing about in the great void.

Lucretius published his meditations exactly two thousand years ago. The two theses I have quoted are still accepted as sound science. We continue to believe that nothing can be made from nothing and that the phenomena of the world must find a final explanation in the behavior of the smallest particles, indivisible and eternal. But it was easier to set up theories and speculate about the ultimate things than it was to add concrete observations and supply details of their operation. In fact we lose little if we omit all the centuries from the days of Democritus and take up the story at a little over a hundred years ago. About that time chemists set up the modern atomic theory of matter and began to investigate and tabulate the properties of all the known elements, and to search for new ones. It was convenient for the chemist to assume that the atoms were indivisible and indestructible, for none of the reagents of the chemical laboratory were powerful enough to change lead into gold, or iron into copper, or any element into any other. Nevertheless, when the properties of the elements were more thoroughly investigated and more and more of the ninety-two elements were identified, it became evident that the ninety-two building units were not chaotic things but were apparently related to one another and could be classified into groups and systems and sub-systems. Whatever their public confession might be, many chemists secretly believed that the atoms were not ultimate things in the sense of Lucretius, and they fully expected that the day would come when atom-smashing would become an indoor sport. In fact, near the close of the century, J. J. Thomson, head of the Cavendish Laboratory at Cambridge, England, actually discovered one of the ultimate units so long dreamed of by philosophers and scientists. He named it an electron. It was not a substance in the ordinary sense but a minute charge of negative electricity. It seemed to be a constituent part of every atom of every element. After two score years scientists still believe that the electron is one of the ultimate things of Lucretius and that no one will ever discover a hammer and an anvil strong enough to crack it open. Everybody is so sure of this that it is perhaps safe to move the negative electron, together with the positive electron discovered in 1931, from the side show of the small into the conservative exhibit in the big show of science. No one now considers an electron a freak.

One of Thomson's students at that time was a certain Ernest Rutherford, who was destined to do more to explain the ultimate nature of things than his distinguished master or any other scientist of our time. Later he succeeded Thomson as the head of the Cavendish Laboratory. He is the hero of my story.

Rutherford was born in New Zealand in 1871 and was educated at schools in Bridgewater and Nelson. The headmaster at Nelson soon recognized that he had found a very unusual youth and in due course the boy was awarded a scholarship at Canterbury College, Christchurch. Here he quickly made his mark by the magnetic detection of wireless waves and other ingenious discoveries. After graduation in New Zealand he received an Exhibition Scholarship for study at Cambridge, England. Someone has remarked that if all the money ever expended for Exhibition Scholarships to others had been absolutely wasted, the granting of this one scholarship to Rutherford more than justified all the expenditures that had been made from the fund. "It was at that time a novelty for a young physicist to arrive at the Cavendish Laboratory from the antipodes," says Professor Eve, "and there was a slight tendency to ridicule. However, formidable questions from the new arrival were received with some awe, and the rumor soon spread that there was 'a young rabbit come from New Zealand who burrows very deep.'"

Rutherford was still on a scholarship and was not yet considered mature enough for the honor of a fellowship when in 1898 he was called to the chair of physics at McGill University in Montreal. This was precisely at the most exciting period in the history of physics. Just one year before, J. J. Thomson had published his discovery of the electron. Three years earlier Roentgen had announced his detection of a new mysterious ray. The very year of Rutherford's arrival the Curies had come upon a marvelous substance called radium. These discoveries did not so much increase knowledge as confuse it. It fastened on science a host of mysteries and contradictions. Enormous domains of ignorance were annexed just when science was coming to feel quite sophisticated and self-important. At McGill University Rutherford was soon joined by a young Englishman named Soddy, who held the title of Demonstrator in Chemistry. The two immediately joined forces to attack and dispel the new chaos that had enveloped science. Rutherford placed a piece of tinfoil over a radioactive substance. The intensity of the action was reduced about a hundredfold. A second piece of tinfoil had no appreciable effect, but when he continued to pile up additional sheets until they were equivalent to a sheet of lead of the thickness of ordinary cardboard, the discharging effect was again suddenly reduced about a hundredfold. Even after this there remained an effect which was still perceptible and which could only be reduced to a negligible amount by a cover of several inches of lead. This was the first demonstration of the fact that radiations from radium-like substances are of three different sorts, which Rutherford named alpha, beta, and gamma rays. All the experiments with radioactive material at this time were very embarrassing and highly erratic. Often a slight current of air would throw all their measurements out of gear. Sometimes everything about the apparatus would itself become radioactive, just like a child catching measles from another child. This matter had to be cleared up before much progress could be made. Rutherford found it to be due to a gas given off by the radioactive substance, which could be wafted about, settle on solids, and make them appear to be radioactive. Rutherford called this gas an "emanation." The gas was merely one of the ninety-two chemical elements that remained radioactive for a few hours and then quieted down. It could be liquefied and even crystallized like any other gas. The gas from radium he called radon.

Many months later it was shown that alpha rays were fast-moving helium atoms, that the beta rays were streams of electrons, and that gamma rays were of the same nature as light waves—in fact, of the same sort as Roentgen or X-rays, only much shorter. Then from the laboratory at McGill came forth in quick succession a large number of startling discoveries. Another remarkable thing happened at this remote and, at that time, little known provincial university. A large number of brilliant advanced students from many parts of the world came to McGill to participate in the new activities. It was soon apparent that Rutherford was not only a youth of blazing genius, but also a young man with a personality and force of leadership rarely seen in the realm of science. He was soon a physicist of world renown, but he always remained accessible to all the ideas his young men brought to him. Indeed it was because of the kindly interest which he showed his pupils that a halo of affection surrounded him wherever he worked. He spread international fame for McGill University and created an unending stimulus for his colleagues and successors at that institution and throughout America. The group that gathered about him came from Poland, Germany, France, England, and the United States as well as from Canada, and his ideals soon penetrated into all walks of science in America. He made several visits to the States, and we had an opportunity to become acquainted at first hand with his remarkable driving ability, his boyish zeal, his kindly human interest, his outspoken frankness, and his approachability.

England could not, of course, permit this genius to remain forever in the provinces. He was called to the University of Manchester in 1907, where he remained until 1919. Here his laboratory became the most productive in the world. His advanced students and co-workers made up a group that now reads like an international directory of modern physicists; among them are Neils Bohr, H. G. J. Mosely, C. G. Darwin, J. Chadwick, H. Geiger, H. R. Robinson, J. M. Nuttall, E. Marsden, D. C. H. Florance, J. A. Gray, R. W. Boyle, H. B. Boltwood, A. Kovarik, G. Hevesy, P. Kapitza, and E. N. daC. Andrade. Everyone has heard of some of these great names.

The twelve years at Manchester were Rutherford's greatest years. In 1911 he set up his nuclear theory of the atom. This view was that an atom consisted of a heavy compact nucleus of positive charge, together with sets of negative electrons swinging about it in planetary fashion. The principal differences in the ninety-two elements consisted in their nuclei, which were light for the light elements and heavy for the heavy elements. If this were true, and if one could crack a heavy nucleus, it would be converted into a lighter nucleus and a transmutation of matter would have taken place. In 1919 Rutherford bombarded nitrogen with fast-moving alpha particles and found that every good hit resulted in changing the nitrogen to oxygen with the release as a by-product of a hydrogen nucleus which he called a proton. This experiment marks one of the landmarks in science. It is the beginning of all the exhibits you now see in the side show of the small, where bombardment of atoms by all sorts of minute bullets is brought about by enormous machines that Science Service tells you about in the Sunday Supplement.

England could be trusted to see that further honors were awarded to Rutherford. In 1914 he was knighted and in 1919 he was given the highest scientific honor that can come to a physicist, namely the headship of the Cavendish Laboratory of Cambridge. Here the researches continued in the same manner as at Montreal and Manchester. "The most outstanding personality in the world," his fellow scientists called him. Brilliant co-workers from everywhere continued to flock to his laboratory. His constant care was that all who worked with him should have full credit for what they did. "He gave away more than he kept for himself," are the appreciative words of one of his students. He excited affection and commanded admiration as he worked with the zeal of a child. There was driving hard work, of course, but no jealousies and bickerings. Every honor came to him that could be accorded a scientist. In 1931 he was raised to the peerage as Lord Rutherford of Nelson. He was the greatest English physicist since Faraday, and in one sense he was more important than Faraday because of the host of great men that went forth from his laboratory. His nickname to his students and co-workers was "Papa."

In October, 1937, this remarkable life came to a sudden end. He was still in the fullness of his powers at the age of only sixty-six. His death was a shock to England and to all the dominions and to the scientific workers throughout Europe, many of whom had been members of his laboratory and all of whom were his friends. On October 25 his ashes were borne to Westminster Abbey, where they rest in the nave near the graves of Newton, Kelvin, Darwin, and Sir John Herschel. Thus another link was forged binding the Empire together, for Rutherford was the first man of science born in the dominions to be buried in that sacred place. The new grave not only honors the genius from overseas, it is also an expression of the changing values that have marked the evolution of British civilization. At first the honor of burial in the Abbey was alloted to holy men, warriors, noblemen, and royalty. In the fourteenth century civilized society had advanced enough to give Chaucer a place within the national shrine. Then in the sixteenth century Edmund Spenser was similarly honored and in the next century Ben Jonson and Beaumont and Drayton, a partial admission of the coming of age of the drama. In the seventeenth century science received its first recognition with the dust of Sir Robert Moray, the first president of the Royal Society, but it was not accorded full honor until early in the next century, with the burial of Newton and his worthy friend and teacher Isaac Barrow, Master of Trinity College.

The last of the classes of men to be entombed or

monumented at Westminster were British statesmen.
I do not know whether this should be interpreted as
marking the decadence or the flowering of English
civilization. However this may be, there remains one
class of the great that is still unrecognized at the
Abbey. Fortunately, however, for the memory of the
British past, there are two Westminster Abbeys and
not one. In the northeast corner of old London just
off Bishopsgate Street and in that small section within
the city walls that escaped the great fire of 1666,
stands the thirteenth-century church of St. Helens.
This is the burial place of the city's great as con-
trasted with the nation's great. Here are entombed
mayors, aldermen, great merchants of the livery companies, ironmongers, cordwainers, mercers, merchant
tailors, fletchers, bowyers, loriners, fishmongers, skin-
ners, vintners, horners, salters, grocers, cloth workers,
upholders, drapers, haberdashers, goldsmiths, sta-
tioners, and representatives of all the other mysteries
that controlled and developed trade and helped to
found the greatness of London and Britain. Most ap-
propriately under an altar of St. Helens lies the body
of Thomas Gresham, mercer, founder of the Royal
Exchange, donor of Gresham College, and the genius
that developed the financial structure of Britain during the reign of Elizabeth. No visit to London is complete without a pilgrimage to the dark interior of
this ancient Westminster of the city. Of course not
all the great merchants are entombed at St. Helens;
many are in forgotten and unmarked graves. It is unfortunate for the completeness of its memorials that

the bodies of Richard Whittington and John Stow, certainly two of the greatest citizens of London, were entombed elsewhere. I am sure that we have not been in the habit of giving sufficient recognition to the courage and abilities of these early London adventurers. They were men of bold enterprise and they sought riches in all parts of the earth. They stood like a rock for the rights of the City of London and for the security and privileges of the trader and the common man. They brought to high honor the title of "Citizen of London" and were, perhaps more than any other class, representative of the temper of British character. They accumulated immense riches, but they gave liberally from their wealth to found churches, hospitals, and homes for the orphaned and the aged, and even built bridges and causeways and water supplies and other public works. But what have these ancient adventurers to do with Lord Rutherford, the hero of this story? Remember that Rutherford, the greatest English scientist of our generation, came from New Zealand. But British stock had first to go forth to the antipodes before the stream of culture could return and complete the circuit. Hence I make the merchant adventurers of ancient London the secondary heroes of my discourse. They are the forgotten men of British greatness. Even the contribution to a cultured life made by the landed aristocracy of England is in part due to the activities of the London traders, for their mission was not only to serve themselves but to enhance the value of land and raise the price of corn and wool and otherwise help create a sound material foundation for church and state. Without the courage and good sense of the London merchants there could have been no great England, no Chaucer, no Shakespeare, no Newton, no Empire. Even America is in part their heir, for the adventurers that founded and built Virginia were supported in part by the guilds of London.

At the close of his life Rutherford believed that four of the building blocks of Lucretius had been discovered. These were the positive and negative electron and the so-called proton and neutron. The proton is the nucleus of the hydrogen atom and its mass is by convention taken to be unity, and similarly its positive electric charge is also by assumption taken to be unity. The neutron, as its name indicates, has no electric charge and its mass is also about unity. Four different things do not seem to give much variety out of which to create a livable universe. No one has as yet offered to undertake the job of building even a small universe from four or from forty things. If the Great Lapidary would grind down the world to dust and grind down that dust to finer dust and continue to grind into finer and finer dust, would there eventually result a dust so fine that it could not be made finer? And would that final dust be of only four or five kinds? Lucretius would have us believe that the grinding would not go on indefinitely. According to his philosophy there would result a dust that could not be made finer. But you should remember that it is not *necessary* to believe this doctrine. You may believe the contrary if you wish and no one can prove you wrong. This is merely an example of the age-mellowed diversity between Anaximander and Empedocles.

Mathematicians and scientific dreamers often claim that there is a limit in the other direction. They assert that the universe is not unbounded in its hugeness. When you happen to find them in a metaphysical mood, they may even claim that the ultimate things of Lucretius and a finite size for the universe are merely complementary concepts; the truth of the one compels the truth of the other. But we must not attempt to follow up such ideas, for the side show of the small is already too big and we must not lug in more freaks. Even Barnum knew that the side shows must not be permitted to outgrow the big top; to hold interest in the side shows you must keep them within reason. There is danger, therefore, that the side show of the small will become too crowded for the good of the circus as a whole. For example, one of the star exhibits is the quantum, or ultimate discrete unit or atom of energy, but even the best of showmen do not know how to interpret all of its acts. There is also a show put on by the mathematicians that some think is entirely too ghostly and mysterious. No doubt one of the next big jobs of science is to move more of the present freak exhibits out of the side shows into the sanity of the big top. Another Rutherford might be able to bring this about.

From four or five kinds of building units of Lucretius you are expected to build a universe and a Garden of Eden and even humanity itself. But could you from such dust build faith and hope and charity? Could you build religion and godliness? Finally, could you from four things compound an intellect that could analyze and comprehend the universe thus created? I wonder if by chance *something has been left out!*

Perhaps you think that I am now attempting to reduce the doctrine of Lucretius to an absurdity. I am not bold enough to say that Lucretius is wrong. I certainly would not put such a claim in writing or announce it publicly. There is a current fashion in science as well as in national dress, and I would no more oppose the doctrine of Lucretius than I would denounce the parade of high heels or condemn the ritual of the cigarette. But in my inner conscience, in no case to be put on paper or spoken aloud, I believe that the thesis of Lucretius is *all wrong* and that the doctrine of the small should be completely reversed. Lucretius was simply guilty of anthropomorphism. The universe as a whole is necessary and sufficient to explain itself, and nothing smaller can fully elucidate or clarify it. The small does not explain the large, but the large explains the small. The universe is a "whole" made up of many lesser "wholes," and the greater gives meaning and value to the lesser. I learn this from General Smuts, who put it in a book, but General Smuts is a warrior and is not afraid of any enemy. I am not a warrior, and I am therefore not courageous enough to confess in public my secret beliefs. If I could put the ideas of General Smuts into a single sentence it would be,

"A 'whole' is more than the sum of its parts," which of course puts a modern Democritus into reverse.

Let one of the marvelous melodies of Beethoven be sounded before a group of listeners. A scientist speaks of the energy of vibration and measures it in units called decibels. But the audience speaks of the beauty and nobility of the melody. The music has life and meaning not because of the decibels but because of the universe in which it is imbedded, which in this case means the group that listens.

That cute little electron bobbing about does not explain the universe; the universe helps explain the electron. The electron has meaning not in itself but only because it is imbedded in a universe. It is anthropomorphic to assert that the earth rules the solar system. As a matter of fact, the earth receives more than it gives out. It is anthropomorphic to believe that the solar system rules the galaxy. As a matter of fact, the solar system receives more than it gives out. It is worse than anthropomorphic to drag into the twentieth century the outmoded philosophy of the Victorian era.

Events flow from the greater to the lesser. Is personality vitalized and given value by the concatenations of electrons, neutrons, and protons, or is it given life and meaning because it fruits from a "whole" more inclusive than itself?

"Step right this way, everybody, to see the magician grind personality into protons!" This makes a good slogan to lure the crowd into the side show, but remember that there are fakes as well as freaks to be found therein. Grind all the things of the earth into dust, you will not thereby explain the Nature of Things. Both Whitehead and Smuts suggest that the "whole" is more than the totality of its pieces. I am glad that I can retain these views in secret and am not obliged to speak out and face the frowns of an anthropomorphic public. I do wish, however, that I could command some form of telepathy to convince you that the struggle of Lucretius and modern scientists to explain the big from the small is not acceptable. Something has been left out!

TO YOUTH

Just at the age twixt boy and youth
When thought is speech and speech
is truth.—SCOTT

The youth of a nation are the trus-
tees of posterity.—DISRAELI

IX

The New Philosophy

PHI BETA KAPPA is a philosophical society. But it is easier to prove this by interpreting the symbol S.P. (*Societas Philosophiae*) on the reverse of the badge than by interrogating the individual members. The confession of faith, as you have heard this evening, is the motto "Philosophy the Guide of Life." The society was born in 1776, when it was quite the fashion to think in terms of such universals as freedom, equality, and inalienable rights; and when it was the habit to dream of a quite perfect world, perhaps very near at hand, where a new and good philosophy would guide us. I do not intend to give too much credit to the lads of the College of William and Mary of one hundred and fifty years ago. The motto was probably easy to adopt because it meant to them that the set of current principles then actually guiding men in the conduct of life did, as a matter of fact, constitute the true faith worthy of all men to be believed. This is generally what we intend when we adopt high-sounding principles. We mean that the philosophy that prevails here and now, that is agreeable to us and is accepted by us, is a proper guide of life. The college boys of '76 did not propose by their motto to invoke allegiance to an unrealized principle, to a principle of life not yet attained, which had to be fought for at great risk. They did not mean to challenge conventional truth or to align themselves with the promoters of the latest fads in philosophy. The motto of the society, then as now, was capable of a gloriously elastic interpretation. Each generation may interpret it as it pleases; in fact, each individual writer of a Phi Beta Kappa address may give it a meaning quite different from that adopted by any other writer. Fortunately our motto can be the text of an infinite number of sermons.

One of my purposes this evening is to recall to you the story of the development of the new learning or the experimental philosophy, as it is called, which took its hold on the world about three centuries ago. I shall attempt to picture especially its development in England, for then I can clothe the figures with familiar garments and can illuminate the story with contemporary gossip more or less familiar to all of you. The second purpose of my address is to appraise the new philosophy and to attempt to pronounce upon it an appropriate verdict, and, finally, to accompany it with as much moralizing as I think the present company will stand.

The contrast between a conventional philosophy and a new or expectant philosophy is always carefully considered by each successive generation. But the new philosophy of one generation may of course become the old philosophy of a later one. Sometimes the world settles down quite content for a long period, studying and disputing in its conventional philosophies until a champion of new thought appears and suddenly breaks up the disputations of the schoolmen. Occasionally the movement gathers the force of a revolution, and a new epoch in human affairs comes into existence. Thus in England in the sixteenth century the old learning was resting quietly in the universities of Oxford and Cambridge. Aristotle and the seven philosophies seemed so safe and so fixed and unchangeable in their human relations that Thomas Gresham in founding his college in London provided that there should be seven professors, one for each of the seven philosophies, and that each professor should lecture once a week, thus providing one lecture a day for each of the seven days of the week.

Thomas Gresham was a merchant and financier, belonging to a family of merchants prominent in English life. He had served Elizabeth his queen and her government on many important fiscal and economic missions. He was the founder of the Royal Exchange and was known as a hardheaded and practical man of extraordinary ability and judgment. Yet this man evidently believed that there was no more likelihood that a new philosophy would be accepted than that the number of days in the week would be increased from seven to eight.

Gresham had evidently long contemplated founding and endowing a college, for the enormous mansion which he built for himself on Bishopsgate Street, a few squares north of the Royal Exchange, was particularly adapted for college use. The building extended around an open court measuring one hundred and forty by two hundred feet. The large section of the edifice on Bishopsgate Street, having a frontage of two hundred feet, contained a great hall twenty by thirty-seven feet and thirty feet high, and two other rooms of practically the same size.

Gresham had some very original ideas. He stipulated that the professors were to be bachelors and were to have apartments in the college. It was also ordained "for comeliness sake that the lecturers should read their lectures in their hoods, according to their degrees in the universities," and that each lecture should be delivered twice, in Latin at eight o'clock in the morning and in English at two o'clock in the afternoon. The Latin lecture was appointed because it was thought "very likely that diverse strangers of foreign countries, who resort to Gresham College and understand not the English tongue, will greatly desire to hear the reading of said lectures, whereby the memory of said founder in erecting of the said college for increase of learning may be divulged to the good example of foreign nations, and the honour and credit of this honourable city." The allotment of the days among the seven philosophies was changed from time to time. One of the early arrangements was as follows:

Sunday	*Divinity*
Monday	*Physic (Medicine)*
Tuesday	*Law*
Wednesday	*Astronomy*
Thursday	*Geometry*
Friday	*Rhetoric*
Saturday	*Music*

THE NEW PHILOSOPHY

When I was admitted to Phi Beta Kappa and the symbols upon the key were explained to me, I was told that the hand at the bottom of the shield was pointing to the seven stars, emphasizing seven, the sacred number, and that the seven stars were the seven philosophies, which should guide the neophyte in Phi Beta Kappa to perfection. I now understand that a Phi Beta Kappa antiquarian has spoiled all this symbolism. I have little sympathy with historians—they are always spoiling good stories; they worship dull facts and seem to have a small opinion of the romance that interests most of us.

*

WHILE Thomas Gresham was planning in 1573 for the propagation and glorification of the seven philosophies, a young freshman named Francis Bacon had entered Trinity College, Cambridge. He was a relative of Gresham's by marriage, being a first cousin of Gresham's wife. He applied himself diligently, but three years taught him to despise the current philosophy of Aristotle. He left Cambridge without a degree, convinced that both the methods and the results of science were erroneous, "yielding," as he said, "no true fruit of learning" but merely idle disputation and schoolish ends. There were planted in him the germs of a new conception. A new method of philosophy must be devised, he insisted, which would serve all mankind, not merely give pleasure and delight to scholars. He claimed that the fortunes of humanity were affected little by its abstract notions of the nature and principle of things. "The aim of all science," he said, "is to endow the condition and life of man with new powers or works, or to extend more widely the limits of the power and greatness of man." He desired that a body of accurately ascertained facts be amassed, from which alone, in his opinion, the processes of nature could be understood and a solid foundation laid for new discoveries and inventions. By such means, he believed, man would attain to "the knowledge of the courses and secret motions of things and the enlarging of the bounds of human empire, to the effecting of all things possible." He held that "there is much ground for hoping that there are still laid up in the womb of nature many secrets of excellent use, having no affinity or parallelism with anything that is now known, but lying entirely out of the beat of the imagination, have not yet been found out. They too, no doubt, will some time or other, in the course and revolution of many ages, come to light of themselves, just as the others did; only by the method of which we are now treating can they be speedily and suddenly and simultaneously presented and anticipated." These doctrines of Bacon were revolutionary; in fact, they brought about an intellectual revolution. Almost instantly the new or experimental philosophy came to the front. It marked the seventeenth century as the beginning of a new epoch.

Hardly were the seven philosophies safely on the daily calendar at Gresham College when the new upstart challenged the completeness of their sacred number. You all know, of course, that the sacred number came to the Hebrews because of their contemplation of the sun, moon, and five wandering stars, one for each day of the week. Bacon added the earth itself as the eighth heavenly body. The new philosophy was to be the philosophy of things near to man, and was to give him for the first time, as Bacon said, empire over the earth and over the forces of nature. Bacon's works had a profound influence, both in England and on the continent. Within twenty years, as we have described elsewhere, a group of vigorous young men in London had taken up the new philosophy, meeting at the Bull-Head Inn in Cheapside to discuss the new or experimental philosophy, and eventually organizing what became the Royal Society of London for the Improvement of Natural Knowledge.

But a strange destiny awaited Gresham College. In 1645 Samuel Foster, professor of astronomy in the College, lectured at two o'clock on Wednesdays. It was the custom of the group of new philosophers, led by Robert Boyle, to attend Foster's lecture and later to repair to Bull-Head Tavern or to the apartments of Dr. Goddard for meat and drink and for discourse and experiment. This led to regular weekly meetings and weekly contributions in money to meet the cost of experiments. Thus Gresham College, with its seven water-tight compartments for the seven philosophies, was itself destined to become an instrument for breaking down the sanctity of the sacred number. Built by Gresham for the perpetua-tion of the old philosophies, it became in the first fifty years of its life the home of the new philosophy.

In the first century of its existence the meetings of the Royal Society were largely given up to experimentation. Thus Gresham College shared with certain of the London inns the honor of serving as the original English laboratory for the experimental learning. The early records of the Society give an interesting picture of the intense eagerness and enthusiasm of the philosophers in the new calling. No distinction was made between pure science and applied science. The following minutes extracted from the record of one of the earliest meetings, that of September 10, 1662, may cause a smile, but there was more good for the future of society bound up in these primitive efforts than in volumes and volumes of disputations on theses of the schoolmen.

"It was order'd, at the next meeting Experiments should bee made with wires of severall matters of ye same size, silver, copper, iron, etc., to see what weight will breake them; the curatour is Mr. Croone.

"Dr. Goddard made an experiment concerning the force that presseth the aire into lesse dimensions; and it was found, that twelve ounces did contract 1/24 part of Aire. The quantity of Aire is wanting.

"My Lord Brouncker was desired to send his Glasse to Dr. Goddard, to make further experiments about the force of pressing the aire into less dimensions.

"Dr. Wren was put in mind to prosecute Mr. Rook's observations concerning the motions of the Satellites of Jupiter.

"Dr. Charleton read an Essay of his, concerning the velocity of sounds, direct and reflexe, and was desired to prosecute this matter; and to bring his discourse again next day to bee enter'd.

"Dr. Goddard made the Experiment to show how much aire a man's lungs may hold, by sucking up water into a separating glasse after the lungs have been well emptied of Aire. Severall persons of the Society trying it, some sucked up in one suction about three pintes of water, one six, another eight pintes and three quarters, etc. Here was observed the variety of whistles or tones, which ye water made at the severall hights, in falling out of the glasse again.

"Mr. Evelyn's Experiment was brought in of animal engrafting, and in particular of making cock spurs grow on a cock's head."

As I have said, each lecture at Gresham College was a double header, delivered in the morning in Latin and later in the day in English. Each meeting of the Royal Society likewise consisted of two events. The most enthusiastic and convivial portion of the membership constituted a dinner group, which met at a tavern once a week to eat and drink, to discourse, and to experiment for about three hours, later to join the fellows of the Royal Society in regular meeting for another three or four hours of the new philosophy. As nearly as I can make out, these enthusiasts put in at least a seven-hour day, which certainly speaks volumes for the drawing power of the new learning. The meeting day shifted from Wednesday to Thursday and back again, finally settling down permanently in 1710 to Thursday. The union of worldly minded and scientifically minded men in the prosecution of the new philosophy was a peculiarly English institution. It was faciliated by the remoteness of the English universities from London and by their type of organization, which permitted the new philosophy to grow up largely independent of Oxford and Cambridge.

On the continent, on the other hand, the new learning was able to get at least one foot in the universities rather promptly. Professor Lorenz recently told me about an interesting episode at the University of Leyden. About 1710 the professor of natural philosophy, who had been presenting the subject by the old book-method of Aristotle, was succeeded by a new professor who evidently had novel ideas about science. Not only did he perform experiments before his hearers, but he filled up some of the rooms with all sorts of brass and glass affairs, cut holes in the shutters, bored holes and drove nails in the floors and ceilings, and was guilty of many other irregular acts. The janitor or caretaker of the building put in a protest and demanded that his pay be increased if he was to care for a building in which so much extra work was put upon him. Secretly he had probably concluded that it was no part of his contract to serve as the keeper of a lunatic. As the university archives show, the janitor's demand was met by the authorities.

But while the revolution in method was sudden, the transition in manner, Professor Lorenz told me, was quite gradual. The professor still continued to adorn himself in impressive professional garments, just as if he were teaching Latin or Greek. Experimental demonstrations performed in conventional professorial dress must have made an extraordinary picture.

Of the men who led British progress in science in the eighteenth century, I shall mention only a few. One of the greatest was Henry Cavendish, who for fifty-two years rarely missed a meeting of the Royal Society. After Cavendish came into his inheritance he was the wealthiest man in England, if not in the world. His house at Clapham, just on the outskirts of London, was undoubtedly the best laboratory in England. He had everything that money could buy in the way of electrical machines, air pumps, and chemicals. His scientific library in Soho Square in the city was open to a host of young scholars who drew books from the rich collection in the same way as Cavendish himself. Then there was Captain James Cook, a sailor but nevertheless a truly great scientist, commanded by an indomitable spirit of adventure and possessed of good sense and a magnificent personality that made him one of the great figures in British history. Perhaps it is not out of place also to mention here our own Benjamin Franklin, who in 1753 received the Copley Medal of the Royal Society. You all know enough about Franklin to understand what I mean when I say that he was a typical example of that combination of man-of-the-world and man-of-science that was so characteristic of the British leaders in the new philosophy.

The eighteenth century was a period of gross animalism, but it was also a period of great enthusiasm, of great physical and spiritual courage, and of great adventure in all fields of learning. There were many patrons of science, men of virility and enterprise. Sir Joseph Banks, for example, spent a lifetime of constant activity in promoting natural knowledge, and devoted enormous sums from his private fortune to the support of all branches of science. He fitted out the good ship *Endeavor* as a floating laboratory, paid for the services of Solander, the favorite pupil of Linnaeas, and enriched the staff with artists, draftsmen, and scientific helpers of all sorts for Cook's memorable three-year voyage of discovery. He not only furnished funds for Captain Cook's voyages but he himself spent three years with Cook in the Pacific. Later he made a voyage of discovery to Iceland and the Arctic Isles.

Joseph Banks holds two unique records. He was for fifty-four years a fellow of the Royal Society and for forty-two years its president. For many years he had to be wheeled to the weekly meetings in an invalid's chair. He introduced to the Royal Society Dining Club a remarkable succession of guests. He had Captain Cook at the club within two weeks of his return from his great voyage, and Captain John Ross and Lieutenant Perry immediately after they returned from their polar expeditions. Herschel he brought around one week after his discovery of the planet Uranus. Now this sort of thing is what makes science worth while. Virility, an abundance or even superabundance of enthusiasm, insatiable curiosity, these must always be the breath of science. Something is lost if science becomes so subdivided, so cellular, as to make no direct appeal to men of the world like Joseph Banks. The modern world is changed, and it must supply a substitute, for science cannot afford to lose the vitality that comes from worldly minded men.

Possibly it was really no loss to the new learning that in England it found no hospitality at the universities and received little support from the government. In no other country did it have a similar history. In England the new learning was born in a tavern, and for several years knew no other home. Science was a city waif; it was a stranger at the universities and remained so until only two or three generations ago. Most of the scientists were amateurs, supported from private fortunes or earning their way in other callings. Newton had hardly enough to live on while he was at Cambridge, for he had to pay for all his instruments, chemicals, and materials out of his own pocket. The fellows of the Royal Society taxed themselves by large fees and dues to pay the cost of their own publications and the expense of their secretaries, their libraries, and their museums. In the second half of the eighteenth century there was probably more good science in the home of Henry Cavendish than in all the colleges of England, and the private libraries of Cavendish and of Joseph Banks, located in their town houses near Soho Square, far exceeded all the other British resources of the day. Only since the World War has the British government offered liberal aid to the new philosophy. Thus in England science has not been a spoiled child. It has fought its way through and made its own career. It is not surprising, therefore, that it has had a virility and a character of its own. There have been compensations in its career of self-support.

ƒ

ALTHOUGH I have spoken particularly of the intellectual revolution in England, the view has not been a partial one so far as mere scientific advance is concerned. During all this time Britannia had been extending her rule throughout the world, while other countries, for the most part, had stayed at home. There has been a difference in results, and a difference in the use of intellectual materials. England did not lose out in the power that came from the new learning, although her great universities only slowly gave recognition to it. In the main they have devoted their efforts to training men in human and spiritual things, primarily for leadership in public life.

The first job of the new learning has been the conquest of the physical world. Its spiritual contributions, although real, have not been so obvious. Three centuries ago man still lived in awe of nature, as he had been living from the day of his creation. He had been limited and ruled by nature as a slave is limited and ruled—everywhere he stood in dread of nature and without mastery over her. Fate represented the great tragic element in life, just as it did in the Greek drama. The new philosophy brought about a reversal of this relationship of man to nature. No longer was it a question of how nature could be prevented from overcoming man, but to what length man might go in subduing nature. He believes he has won the mastery—not complete, it is true, but with the balance of control in his favor. This consciousness of power has changed the human outlook. Man now doubts the necessity of many of the hardships of life which he formerly regarded as inevitable. Not alone have the fear of the Black Death and the dread of lightning and the perils of the sea vanished. Man has come to believe that many of the common hardships of daily life, the cruel pressure of economic forces, the withholding of freedom and of equal opportunity, are unnecessary and intolerable. He now knows that disease can be cured, that life can be prolonged, that much human suffering can be prevented. The control over natural processes given him by science, the control over human happiness given him by modern medicine, he is now convinced must be matched by a control over destiny itself. Man has not yet achieved this mastery, but he believes in its possibility. He is no longer willing to bow down to fate nor to resign himself to all the tragic elements in life, as did the ancients; he is demanding deliverance through the researches of economic science and through the understanding of history.

The World War has taught him that his great power over the processes of nature may be used quite as much for his destruction as for his advancement. The new philosophy that produces a thousand tons of poison gas in a day and tens of thousands of machines and aeroplanes to discharge it, is not a philosophy that of itself will lead men to better things. The new philosophy suddenly finds itself challenged, and doubted, and questioned as never before in the three hundred years of its history. A prayer goes up for a new principle and for a new pilot to serve as the guide of life. Perhaps the world must await a new Francis Bacon with a new message of deliverance. Perhaps only an old-fashioned philosophy and old-fashioned standards are needed. But in any case a fundamental regeneration of spiritual forces must be set in action. The new philosophy of Bacon is fast becoming an old philosophy. The scientific revolution has advanced man farther in his control over nature than in his control over himself. When millions of lives may be obliterated by a chemical formula, a subjugation of human selfishness is needed as never before.

And poison gases are not the only compounds that threaten society. Modern business methods and the modern system of industrial development contain poisons and explosives more destructive, perhaps, than material reagents. If we cannot establish control over the selfishness of men, these powers will tend to become more threatening and more ruthless until civilization itself will be in danger. An essential principle of the new philosophy must be the replacement of the law of the jungle by a higher law. Only through the reign of unselfishness can humanity realize its ideals. This is of course nothing more than the fundamental altruism of Christianity, one of the oldest of truths but one of the hardest to accept. To establish this axiom in human affairs is still a great task for the future. The power-creating sciences have outrun the power-controlling sciences. The danger lies in the difficulty of stimulating progress in the power-controlling sciences. A thoughtful economist has said that "there is danger that the natural sciences must always outstrip the social sciences. In the first place, the natural sciences can use the experimental method, and the social sciences have hardly yet devised an adequate substitute. Then again in the natural sciences the inventor and original thinker is rewarded and honored, but in the social sciences the inventive mind is more or less ostracised and new ideas that touch upon the key problems of modern life, namely, the control of human and economic activities, are at once branded as radical and dangerous."

For this reason I believe that the universities in America may have little to do with the development of the philosophy of the coming century. They do not seem to be generating grounds for courage and virility. I expect, therefore, a reversal in the position of university influence. In England the spiritual control may grow and spread from the universities. In America I expect the hope of the new philosophy to lie, not with the university faculties, but with men of the world; with leaders in the industries; with engineers and business men and lawyers and men close to affairs. We must look for a new Christopher Wren, who can look upon life as a whole; for a new James Cook, who is unafraid to put ahead in the blackest sea; for a new Henry Cavendish, who will devote his fortune and his life to the advancement of ideas precious to his fellow men. The new philosophy must be the philosophy of the control of man's power over himself. The issue is for the youth of this and of the next generation. I am glad that the outcome seems to be in doubt; for this doubt is needed to tempt the conscience of the world's youth, and to challenge them to prove their worth.

The Self-Training of a Teacher

FORTY-FIVE years ago this very day—almost this very hour—I began my university teaching at Wisconsin. I cannot think of anyone less prepared in technical psychology and pedagogy for such a position. Experimental psychology was then just beginning, and the science of education was groping about like a small child. Perhaps, therefore, I should also say that I know of no one who at that date was better prepared in technical pedagogy for university instruction. I started off with four daily classes of forty freshmen each and an advanced class of two students, which soon dwindled to one. The universities of America have always been generous, even overgenerous, in supplying an abundance of students to their green and utterly inexperienced tutors. I was so unsophisticated that I could think of no finer job than to teach mathematics to freshmen. Until quite recently I thought that everybody was of the same opinion. It was a shock to me to learn that some think that there is a higher job.

But actually I did not teach freshmen. I taught attorneys, bankers, big business men, physicians, surgeons, judges, congressmen, governors, writers, editors, poets, inventors, great engineers, corporation presidents, railroad presidents, scientists, professors, deans, regents, and university presidents. For that is what those freshmen are now, and of course they were the same persons then.

I was teaching with such enthusiasm and was so proud of my classes that it never occurred to me that my work could be criticized. It was the self-confidence and conceit of a beginner. But President Bascom visited my classes. After each visit I was called to his office. He went over things with me criticizing at length, but justly and with uncanny precision and directness, calling upon his imagination to say something pleasant at the end. Why did President Bascom take such trouble with an insignificant tutor? It was because he knew that I was not teaching freshmen, but the men I have mentioned. That is the first lesson that the university teacher must learn. Our contact with students must not be for a moment nor at a point, but through the complete trend of a life, the years to come being of one substance with the present. We must be ready by our magic to unroll the long scroll of a life before us to the epoch of the present or to the epoch of the future, as we will. A prophet once exclaimed: "Behold the dawn! Behold the dawn! The things as yet but half declared command the coming day."

The second lesson the young teacher must learn is to become an artist in handling human material. He should know what is going on deep in the brain of each of his students. This may not appear in the manuals of pedagogy, but nevertheless this difficult duty is ours. In those wonderful years following adolescence, when the pulse is steadying to a firmer beat, youth seems to cover himself with a cloak of diffidence and timidity. The new man is imminent but hidden from view. He will hardly confess to his own father the plans and ambitions, the dreams of service that lie deep in his conscience. To the superficial teacher he seems a trifler, but that is only the garb he assumes to hide his first aspirations to man's estate. Few young men are really triflers. Way back deep in the head of nearly every youth is the ambition and the determination to make something fine out of his life. Let the teacher discover his way to this hidden place and build his influence upon it. The teacher must train himself to be an artist in human material.

The third lesson for the college teacher to learn is the art of making his subject interesting. It is not his task to teach interesting things, as the quacks proclaim, but to make interesting the things that must be taught. He must teach the basal sciences as they exist, and it is his task to make the things they contain a part of a living world, full of the adventure and the hazards of learning. This, of course, is the reason why an instructor must be highly trained and productive in his special field and widely read in the history of science, and also have some knowledge of the literature of the race.

This last point deserves further elaboration, especially for the younger instructors. It is a sad experience to visit a classroom and discover many rich personalities on the students' side of the rostrum but a weak or undeveloped personality on the teacher's side.

It is obvious that the teacher will find great difficulty in overcoming this potential difference. How may the teacher develop a rich personality? Unfortunately there are no psychological calisthenics that can transform a weak into a rich personality. It is largely a matter of inheritance. Luckily, however, it is not a matter of family but of racial inheritance. We are all mentioned in the wills of Homer and Shakespeare and of all the great masters of letters; we do not share merely in part, but each of us inherits in full all their rich chattels. You may be assured that great literature, great history, and great biography belong to us—even to mathematicians—and may be claimed and cultivated as our own. Hence the students have a right to find something more in the classroom than the narrow mechanics of a scientific machine. Instead of twenty times at the movies, better the guest of Homer twenty times. What has Homer to do, you will ask, with the teaching of mathematics? I use Homer, of course, merely as an example. His heavy-breasted heroes contending in the sweat of their primal passions are reacting to the same emotions that sway men everywhere, and to motives that rule our own destiny. As you follow the story of their strife the fibers of your being will vibrate with the ambitions and angers universal among humanity; your personality will quicken to a new appreciation of the facts of life. In other words, the ingredients necessary to compound a man can hardly be omitted from the recipe for making a teacher. You need not be afraid, therefore, to enrich your life by the cultivation of letters and by indulgence at the feast of the humanities.

If it were not for the demand of interest, perhaps we could standardize our work by questionnaires and turn the classroom over to the radio or the phonograph. Especially important is the history of your own specialty. The student needs to know the source of some of the great discoveries and the form and texture of their primitive formulation. Let him learn that one of the earliest physicists and hydraulic engineers was a barber of Alexandria two thousand years ago. From the money saved from shaves and haircuts he built the first valve pump and the first fire engine. If the student will inspect a village pump today, he will find the same curious curves to the hand brakes and to the air chamber as were adopted by Ctesibius twenty centuries ago. He will note in studying the history of technology that the useless ornamental scrolls on the handle of a handsaw are the same as were used in Egypt five thousand years ago. The student may forget formulas, but he will not soon forget the story of Archimedes running through the streets of Syracuse naked from the baths, shouting "Eureka! Eureka!" The reason is that these are human interest stories. Science is news, and at one time some of the items we teach would have been first-page write-ups, had there been such a thing. Archimedes with his Eureka incident would have commanded a "banner spread." Human interest comes first, but a second purpose of introducing the history of science is to demonstrate that knowledge is a growing organism linked intimately with human progress.

But mathematics has a present and a future as well as a past. Its contacts with the other sciences and its application to some of their major problems must not be unknown to the teacher. He will find ample opportunity to make his instruction more interesting by limited use of such erudition. Students are interested in the power as well as in the romance of the giant we call mathematics.

Further, the instructor must maintain a creative contact with research in some field of learning. This observation is so trite and commonplace that I am ashamed to make it. But I mean more by it than is commonly intended. It is the creative attitude toward all phases of life, not merely toward a specialty, that I would emphasize. I learned this lesson from President Bascom years ago at college rhetoricals. The theme of his discourse was the three attitudes of the individual toward the universe: first, the cognitive attitude, founded upon the desire to know; second, the esthetic attitude, founded upon the desire to recognize and appreciate the full beauty of existence; third, the ethical attitude, founded upon the desire to achieve the highest good. I do not believe that there was anything new in that topic—very likely the theme goes back to Aristotle; but the novelty lay in what followed, for then came John Bascom's powerful exposition of the duties of life that each attitude implies. It was the duty of everybody, not merely of specialists, to add year by year to the store of human knowledge;

it was the duty of everybody, not of poets and artists alone, to contribute day by day to the beauty of the world; it was the duty of everybody, not of a few leaders of men, to make hour by hour the world a better place in which to live. The virility and power with which all this came forth I cannot, of course, picture nor describe. It was the radiation from a prophet. It entered my frame and put there a tenseness that has never vanished—it changed in an instant the dynamics of my life.

I learned that day that we are not only teachers of mathematics but philosophers of the good life. The duty is pressed upon us of enriching and refining all contacts with the world and of handing on the spirit of it to our students.

The teacher cannot accomplish everything. Perhaps it is more in his power to enrich the personality of the student than to develop his mentality. The teacher can train the student in the facts of his subject; he can drill into him the technical skill required; he can develop in him a proper attitude toward learning; and, most of all, he can train him in proper habits of work and of self-expression. But the teacher soon comes up against a stone wall. The God-given abilities of the student, the inborn qualities necessary to success, the teacher can neither create nor augment. Education wins many victories, but there are vast domains it cannot penetrate. The supreme triumph of the educational process is the case of Helen Keller. All the training that a teacher can give is there illustrated by an example that everyone can understand. But the God-given abilities were present in Miss Keller in the beginning, and antedated the work of the teacher—gifts that were not transferable and that the teacher did not create. Our freedom and the freedom of the student is harshly limited by nature. We are propelled by many engines within us over which we can exert only slight control. We are propelled by our inheritance—by the powerful engine of heredity. We are propelled by our emotions—fear, vanity, and so on, and by all the range of animal passions and appetites. We are propelled by the forces of habit—"our past actions press mightily upon us for repetition." But here lies the golden opportunity of the teacher. He has marvelous power to develop the formative forces of habit before it is too late. Mathematics here holds a central position and its classrooms are the best laboratories for the development of intellectual and scholarly habits. We teachers of mathematics recognize and gladly accept these responsibilities.

In bringing this brief discourse to a close, I well know that I have not said what you expected me to say, nor what you wished me to say. You desired, I am aware, a discussion of concrete items of technique. You wished to know of standardized procedures, supported by questionnaires and comparative tests. I have deliberately and knowingly seen fit to disappoint you. I have done this because I feel the need at the present moment of placing the emphasis on the temper and the spirit of our duties, rather than on their technique. Teaching is more than an art to be practiced— it is a life to be lived. At the present moment it is important to stress the activities that are attractive to the gifted teacher. There is urgent need to insist upon a teaching staff of virile and catholic personal qualities. We must have help at this point from the faculties and from all the university authorities, and from the public. The greatest obstacle to the attraction of gifted men and women to the teaching profession, and the greatest discouragement to their continued enthusiasm and success, is the wide-open admission to the freshman class of incompetents and the mentally dull. Certain inborn abilities must be brought to college by the student himself—the university can neither create nor augment them. Some selection, some rejection, much encouragement to the gifted student (whether rich or poor) is a St. Peter's job at the college gate. Stanford University, California Institute of Technology, and a few others have shown the way. Unless we can restrict college admissions to those who possess a minimum of innate ability, no amount of pedagogy, no amount of instructional skill, and no amount of enthusiasm and self-training can prevail. A beginning in the selective admission of students is being made—it should be hastened and the public should support it. Other conditions seem favorable; the competition for positions is becoming keener, the salaries are slowly moving to a higher level, and the qualifications for the doctor's degree tend to become more exacting. It has seemed well, therefore, for me to emphasize the higher qualities the teacher should develop by careful self-training and whole-hearted devotion to his students. He can be assured that there is no vocation where there are so many good things to do and that leads so readily to contentment and the sense of victory. Although by temperament and other qualities I was ill adapted to the life of a teacher, I wish to testify after all these years that it is indeed the good life we attain—I am sustained and confirmed by its many rich rewards.

Heaven's Highway

IN AN address delivered before the Wisconsin chapter of Phi Beta Kappa just fifteen years ago I said: "Phi Beta Kappa is a philosophical society. But it is easier to prove this by interpreting the symbol S. P. (*Societas Philosophiae*) on the reverse of the badge than by interrogating the individual members. The confession of faith, as you have heard this evening, is the motto 'Philosophy the Guide of Life.' The society was born in 1776, when it was quite the fashion to think in terms of such universals as freedom, equality, and inalienable rights; and when it was the habit to dream of a quite perfect world, perhaps very near at hand, where a new and good philosophy would guide us. I do not intend to give too much credit to the lads of the College of William and Mary of one hundred and fifty years ago. The motto was probably easy to adopt because it meant to them that the set of current principles then actually guiding men in the conduct of life did, as a matter of fact, constitute the true faith worthy of all men to be believed. This is generally what we intend when we adopt high-sounding principles. We mean that the philosophy that prevails here and now, that is agreeable to us and is accepted by us, is a proper guide of life. The college boys of '76 did not propose by their motto to invoke allegiance to an unrealized principle, to a principle of life not yet attained, which had to be fought for at great risk. They did not mean to challenge conventional truth or to align themselves with the promoters of the latest fads in philosophy."

The fifteen years that have elapsed since these words were spoken have brought about many changes. For one thing, I can no longer take a facetious delight in referring to Phi Beta Kappa as a "philosophical society," for during this period the youth of the world has been aroused to a philosophic outlook on life and in his daily work demonstrates his faith in our motto. Youth asks questions as never before. He is more eager to catechise his seniors than to be catechised by them. He asks, for example: "Why be born at all, if one must be born into a misfitted world?" Youth is swept with a passion to search out the cause of our woes. Problems of national and world betterment seem very close to him—much closer than fifteen years ago. He is eager to battle for the validation of his now invalid world. He does not question that philosophy is a trustworthy guide of life.

I assume that the originators of our society did not use the term philosophy in a narrow technical sense. They did not intend to impose upon youth the midnight study of Descartes, Leibnitz, Kant, and the others. The founders of the society used the term, as I intimated fifteen years ago, to describe a thoughtful and unimpassioned approach to life's problems, and an unemotional contemplation of the experiences of ancient and modern peoples. The lifelong persistence in such a habit, our founders believed, would lead to that final attainment we call wisdom.

I am sure that I have described correctly the normal attitude of the modern youth toward the perplexities of the day. He seeks the good life in the spirit of Phi Beta Kappa. But it is equally obvious that these past fifteen years have also witnessed the rise of a school of thought contradictory to the teachings of our society. This school proposes to regiment youth and provides a plan that frees him from all necessity of thinking for himself; it brands as absurd the Phi Beta Kappa view that philosophy, or any other individually pursued exploration, can lead us toward the good life. This new channel into which it is sought to force youth, this newly discovered shortcut to eternal bliss, I call "Heaven's Highway," because of its close analogy to the modern concrete structure on which youth is also invited to speed to his destiny. "Heaven's Highway," like its concrete analog, is fenced high with billboards, telling him just what to think and just what to do. On the physical road the billboards tell us of the luxurious hotels that await us, of the exhilarating beverages that will inspire us, and of the many cures for human ills that can be bought by the bottle. The information planted along the highway is apparently the work of philanthropists—who are only too glad to pay good money for the rent of land and for the cost of steel and lumber and printer's ink, merely to aid us in the pleasures of the journey.

All this has its counterpart on that hypothetical road I call "Heaven's Highway." Youth is started on the imaginary pavement, billboarded to the skies with propaganda for the journey. On the mythical highway we are directed to spiritual sanctuaries of soothing luxury, to mental stimulants of great potency, to political cures for every social ill, all trumpeted at youth with the self-assurance of a congress of quacks. It would be treason to suggest that youth should participate in his own guidance. He must hide or destroy his Phi Beta Kappa key. In Italy Heaven's Highway is billboarded in beautiful pastel colors; in Germany the billboards are much the same, but done in hideous combinations of black and white. The Heaven's Highway of Russia is advertised as the best and only direct route to immortal blessedness, but it is not a highway at all. It is an endless tunnel and the propaganda shines forth upon youth from top and bottom as well as from both sides. In such a narrow, one-way tunnel the deviations suggested by the doctrine of Phi Beta Kappa would lead only to destruction and to the complete blocking of the traffic. In Russia it is Phi Beta Kappa versus OGPU.

Where do these new paths lead? The new autocrats say to paradise, but our Phi Beta Kappa philosophy warns us that they lead toward a new world

> *Wherein the beast was ever more and more,*
> *But man was less and less.*

What about Heaven's Highway in America? Are we also engaged in building an arterial route to paradise? It is obvious that we are in no position to throw bricks at Mussolini or Hitler or Stalin. The Heaven's Highway that the propagandists are attempting in America differs little from those abroad except for the worse. Our billboards and propaganda are more inconsistent and more contradictory, uglier and more dangerously placed. The newspaper propagandists have attempted more than Mussolini and have been approached for sheer absurdity only by Hitler and Stalin. They are trying to move a multitude of institutions to the side of Heaven's Highway—churches and schools and even courts of law, where they may become better agents of propaganda. For example, those hot-dog stands serving finely ground and highly spiced pabulum in uniform and equally spaced links; are these not the colleges that have moved to the roadside to nourish wayfarers by means of standardized capsules with contents ground and spiced and stuffed by their professors? But the American colleges as a group are sound. Only a few of them have set out on Heaven's Highway to engage in the hot-dog activity. You cannot canalize American education, for our colleges have been brought up in the traditions of Phi Beta Kappa.

The keepers of the billboards in America fall into two rather contradictory classes. First, there is a large section of the press, screeching at youth and urging him forth upon the smooth concrete of Heaven's Highway. Their urgings tend strongly to the right. Then there is another class of propagandists made up of a section of the writers of modern literature. Their pull is strongly to the left. Perhaps we could safely leave these contradictory billboards to outface each other and nullify each other's influence. But it would be best to demolish both of them, for they are an ugly sight and their influence is evil and unwanted.

The propaganda of the press is fallacious because it undertakes to guide youth by the burning issues of the current moment, by the prejudiced and unverified motives of the present hour. It has little use for the philosophical view of the past or for the long view of human progress. It has eyes only for the current panorama and for today's and tomorrow's profit. Unfortunately current events are the very happenings that no one understands. To attempt to see through them leads only to confusion and to the blurring of vision. In the current panorama we see too much and we see too little. We see too much because we see the shadows; we see too little because we do not see the details obscured by those shadows. But when the current panorama has receded, when it has joined the past, when we see the picture reflected in memory's mirror, then the shadows are dissolved, and the details emerge and perhaps we may even begin to comprehend the scene in part. The current mix of new events is usually a fog obstructing the far view. The Greeks put the matter in stronger language. Ajax, in the midst of his perplexity and facing his calamity, exclaimed:

All new events the multitudinous years bring forth
To shadow me from all I know.

To Ajax that was the final fact. Current events had proved to be a device of the gods to confound and confuse him, and to shadow him from the truth he really knew.

I base my condemnation of the writers of modern

fiction of the youth-propagandist type upon the fact that their product is not art and cannot possibly develop into art. And these writers are themselves ready to admit the charge. They claim that their interest is life itself, and hence their work need not be art. I should be glad to meet them on either claim. They seem to possess a naïve view of the nature of youth and of the manner in which he may be influenced.

Let me contrast their methods with the ancient manner of presenting the human story to the public. Consider first the simple story of the Iliad. It starts naturally with a not too great piece of wickedness. Paris is a handsome and marvelously attractive personality, and Helen is the most beautiful and delectable woman of her day. In the age-long rivalry among those who have sought to glorify Helen, no one has excelled the poet who exclaimed:

> *Oh! thou art fairer than the evening air,*
> *Clad in the beauty of a thousand stars.*

The elopement of the twain would appear to be so natural an event that it could hardly form the basis of a modern short story. But it was more than an elopement. It involved, among other things, the violation of the hospitality of a host. Measured as wickedness was measured in that ancient time, the initial transgression must be said to have been ample. Christopher Marlowe is wrong. It was more than Helen's face "that launched a thousand ships and burnt the topless towers of Ilium." But think of the world-shaking calamities that followed. Ten years of battle and siege and the loss of many heroes of many lands. Then the destruction of a royal family and the leveling to a mere mound of the proud city of the Troad. The enormous calamities seem disproportionate to the initial transgression. But this was the Greek way of it. The initial wickedness as measured in human units need only be sufficient to warrant the story. The final catastrophe must be meted out not in human units but in the huge units of measure used by the gods. The scales and stadia of the gods, not those of man, must measure out the final calamity. In the hour of reckoning we are conscious of the giant tread of super-beings and we hear the crash of bronze on Olympus. "Vengeance is mine," voiced by a god, is in substance the closing line of every Greek tragedy. When it is over we exclaim, "What a pygmy is man, flung by his transgressions into that whirl of destiny!"

You say that such treatment of a story is not true to life. I know that, but it is the highest art. You reply that art is not life. I know that also. But the radiations from art, those waves proceeding from great art and penetrating the inner spirit of youth, those radiations are of the very substance of life. Art is not life; it is the halo of life. Life has to do with men and nature; art has to do with the ghosts that rule both of them. Art and religion are not life, but no worth-while life can be sustained without the penetrating rays that emanate from both these universals.

The modern writer of fiction has a contempt for all of this. He has no use for art; he is interested in life; he is, he claims, a realist. Sometimes he also starts his story with a huge piece of wickedness, but instead of developing a final calamity on the plan of the classics, he allows the fatal consequences to ooze out slowly into the blood stream of his characters, culminating in an uncertain and asymptotic ending. The piece of wickedness that initiates the story is intended to introduce youth to a real view of a part of this naughty world. The propagandist does not hesitate to proclaim the sins of humanity in all their grossness; in fact, the fiction writers portray the sins of the world with such grossness that there is no need for the six hundred pages that follow. The first chapter should be the last, for if, as the author claims, his scene is laid in a real world, then all human experience shows that a huge burden of wickedness sinks and keeps submerged anyone who attempts to carry it. The real world has found a way to eliminate the six hundred pages of consequences.

Perhaps the most effective fiction propaganda is of the newspaper reportorial type, featuring the horrors of factory and slum, where society itself is the villain of the piece. What has been said about the front-page propaganda of the press applies also to this type of writing. It is conceivable that if the story could be given the artistry and vision and genius of a Dickens, it might well be judged on a higher plane, on the plane of an adequate philosophy of life. But there is nothing more terrible, as Dostoevski once said, than realism that sees no further than the end of its nose.

If the propagandist is to become a realist he must conform to the facts of life. We are as much in the dark as ever concerning many phases of life. There are numerous uncertainties and surprises in any human story. But our knowledge has advanced. It has moved on to a few sound and well-established principles. One of these is the conception of Professor Whitehead, General Smuts, and other modern thinkers that life consists of "wholes" or "organisms" which function in the universe as distinct and easily recognized entities or units. Each whole contains numerous ingredients, many of them seemingly contradictory but all necessary to the whole. In the complete whole or organism many of the evil or unwholesome elements become wholesome and good, and much of the evil we note may also be reckoned as good. General Smuts emphasizes that the whole is not the sum of its parts but a new organism to be judged by its total qualities and functions.

To illustrate what is meant by a whole, I might call your attention to a single cell of living matter, with all its parts and ingredients, whose total behavior, in some mysterious way, is more than the sum of the chemical and physical activities of its parts. But for present purposes I must use a more complex example, even though a very crude and unsatisfactory one. Let us suppose we see a tigress tearing apart and utterly destroying an antelope. The cruelty and ruthlessness of the act arouses our anger. We find ourselves condemning, if not actually throwing bricks at the tigress. But General Smuts would call our attention to the fact that we are observing only a single short incident in the lives of tiger and antelope and not completely observing even that. That same tigress may be a good mother to its cubs. She keeps them clean and sanitary and trains them in grace and beauty. Even the savage act itself has another interpretation. The tigress is contributing to the swiftness and agility and hence to the beauty of antelopes. This statement seems grotesque, but it is true, nevertheless, that if there were no beasts of prey, antelopes would not develop their agility and their beauty. If we consider a sufficiently inclusive totality, namely, a totality of the hunters and the hunted, we see that the element of cruelty is absorbed as a necessary ingredient in a more perfect whole. My illustration is crude, but its very crudity tends to explain the manner in which General Smuts has made a beginning, in his theory of holism, toward the solution of the age-long riddles of sin and suffering.

I will give another crude illustration. Let the whole we are considering be made up of a married couple. Let us suppose that the man possesses the average or normal number of shortcomings. If he is carrying a huge burden of wickedness he will sink, and the whole we have assumed will be destroyed. But we are assuming only the normal amount of shortcomings. Let us trace their influence on the whole. You may be sure that the wife soon knows all about the iniquities of her man. The effect on her is to develop self-confidence, a sense of excellence, and a superiority complex which enables her to hold her head high and meet the world with new courage. The shortcomings of the man emerge in the whole as a victory for the woman. The shortcomings turn out to be a useful ingredient in a perfect whole.

It is of course no part of a gentleman to suggest that the wife may also possess shortcomings, and I make no such suggestion. But for the purpose of this Phi Beta Kappa addresss I shall propose a purely hypothetical case. Let us assume, as a working hypothesis, that the wife also possesses shortcomings. These will forever remain unknown to her, but they become fully known to the man. They inspire in him a new sense of confidence, they build up his superiority complex, and in consequence he faces the world with a new sense of victory. Thus we arrive at the paradox that a whole may be made more perfect because of its imperfect ingredients.

It is not expected, of course, that a modern philosopher will be understood. In fact, as soon as he is understood he is out of date and as good as dead. The very life blood of modern philosophy is its incomprehensibility. The women's afternoon reading circles will drop Bergson or any other philosopher at once if anyone claims to understand him. I have discovered the proper way to read modern philosophy. Read two or three chapters—two or more times if necessary. If nothing happens, and usually nothing does happen, go on to the next chapter. Whenever you experience a new sensation in your head, a sensation, for example, something like a tennis ball bounding from front to back and from side to side, stop at once. That sensation is an idea that has broken loose. Write down immediately in your own words the sensation you have experienced. I have used this method in studying a philosophic discourse on Beauty. I give you the result in my own language, boiling down several chapters into a single definition. It helps to illustrate "the utility of opposites," an important idea in the modern theory of holism:

"I define that indefinable thing called Beauty as that which exists if and only if it be accompanied by a small portion of that other indefinable thing called ugliness; and I define that indefinable thing called ugliness as that which exists when and only when it is accompanied by a small portion of that other indefinable thing called Beauty."

The simplicity and clarity of this definition must appeal to all of you. It is several chapters, remember, reduced to a single sentence.

I can also bring home to you the significance of the modern theory of holism and the utility of opposites by a very simple but very blunt question: Who would wish to be kissed on the cheek by an angel? I can think of no more chilling experience. On the contrary, a little sin is warm to the touch; saints and archangels are hard to fit into any theory of holism. Angels make dull pals. To complete a character there must be enough frailty, but not more than enough, to be worthy of forgiveness. We are bound to each other not only by our virtues, but by the forbearance and forgiveness we must grant, each to each, because of our shortcomings. It requires opposites to complete a whole. "Good men write bad hymns," says Yeats, and I assume that bad men write good hymns because their need of mercy is so great. You must not infer that I believe that there is not great need for a vast development of virtue in humanity. I simply mean that man is a bundle of opposites; that a world of perfect human beings, of beings without passions, angers, sins, and forgiveness of sins, would be a realm that we are unable to imagine. It would be a world in which the current canons of art and of religion could not prevail. The joy of existence, strange to say, seems to be bound up in a mystical polarity with the sorrows of the race.

I have sought to make clear that the writer who hopes to propagandize youth gains little by forsaking art for realism. He is discarding the greater for the lesser force. Every normal youth has in his personality something of the heroic. He wishes to attain command, to attain complete command over himself and as much command over his environment as may be practicable. The appeal to the heroic in youth is perhaps the best approach for any teacher. Every university man knows that youth cannot be influenced by precept, nor can he be influenced by the tabulation of facts. The open road to youth is through the radiations from great literature. Shall I exclude science and mathematics from this influence? Yes, if they are a mere tabulation of events. But so far as the natural and social sciences are the story of great deeds, so far as they describe a thrilling adventure into mysteries, or tell of hard-fought victories over error, or recite the drama of the conquest of the unknown, so far as these sciences are seen to be revelations of this sort, they too are masterpieces, although written in part by nature itself.

There are two charges against modern youth: one that he is a radical and the other that he is a pacifist. The first charge is true and has been true for centuries. Ever since the dawn of modern science, youth has been radical. This trait has no serious implication —it is merely an expression of the natural altruism of youth. When I was in college nearly all the students were absorbed in the writings of Henry George. The single tax was a favorite subject of debate in the literary societies. As a matter of fact, we had no comprehension of the things Henry George was writing about. We did not know what it was all about, but we thought we did. We were impressed with his tone of honesty and his serious approach to the problem of human betterment. Most of us would have announced ourselves as converts had it not been for our professor of political economy. We were afraid he would condition us. We, the youth of my day, like the youth of all generations, stood for the betterment of everything, everywhere, and we were ready to paint the universe with rainbows. It was only a little flaming of romance; no one, I am sure, would have wished to quench it. But by the time we reached the age of thirty we had become as sophisticated and as hardboiled as the general run of men, and at forty we had become impossible. Youth is still altruistic and is still accused of radicalism by his elders. What is needed is not less altruism but the invention of some new form of altruism that will not evaporate at thirty, that will last, in part at least, until the age of forty or fifty or even sixty. The disease from which the small group of parading and placarding and picketing and orating radicals in the universities is suffering is not radicalism; it is lack of a sense of humor, the most devastating and incurable disease to which youth is subject. A sense of humor will prove a staunch prop to a good philosophy of life.

The charge of pacifism is also true, but we must not forget that there is no contradiction between pacifism and patriotism. Youth, in any crisis of national danger, will be too eager rather than too slow to defend his flag. I can prove to you that there is no contradiction between pacifism and patriotism. One of the most damning indictments against war was written in ancient Greece by a national hero, one who had fought at Marathon and had won glory at Plataea and Salamis. He called Ares, the god of war, a cheating money-changer, giving back in exchange for the people's gold only the dust of heroes. You could not hurl a harsher epithet at an Athenian than to call him a cheating money-changer. I will read you the quotation. Remember that it is Aeschylus speaking, a hero of Marathon, Plataea, and Salamis, and the greatest of the Greek dramatists. The occasion is the return of the straggling armies of the victors from the ten long years of the siege of Troy:

> *Each home that sent its master far away*
> *From Hellas' shore*
> *Feels the keen thrill of heart, the pang of*
> *loss, to-day.*

For, truth to say,
The touch of bitter death is everywhere!
Familiar was each face, and dear as life,
That went unto the war,
But thither, whence a warrior went of old,
Doth nought return—
Only a spear and sword, and ashes in an urn!
For Ares, lord of strife,
Who doth the swaying scales of battle hold,
War's money-changer, giving dust for gold,
Sends back, to hearts that hold them dear,
Scant ash of warriors, wept with many a tear,
Light to the hand, but heavy to the soul;
Yea, fills the bronze urn full
With what survived the flame—
War's dusty measure of a hero's frame!

The last line of this quotation you may wish to add,
in imagination, to the words engraved on the cenotaph
of the Unknown Soldier at Arlington, so that the complete inscription might read:

Here rests in honored glory, an American Soldier
Known only to God.
War's dusty measure of a hero's frame!

The added line completes the story. It describes war,
war with its glory, with its horror.

§

A FEW WEEKS AGO I paid a visit to the University of
Cuba. It was a pleasure to find that that country had
attempted to honor learning by the liberal equipment

and embellishment of its university. The most prominent place in the city had been selected for its home—a veritable Acropolis, adorned with many harmonious and beautiful buildings. As a formal entrance to that group of temples, a grand stairway scores of meters in breadth had been cut in the face of the cliff. There, on a landing on the stairway, had been erected a heroic figure of Alma Mater. The benign face of the good mother bore a smile of welcome to the ascending host of students, and her arms were slightly extended as if to clasp youth to her bosom with the love of a mother. Yet that university had been closed for six years, and in all the buildings and lecture halls there had been quartered, not faculty and students, but an army of soldiers with rifles and machine guns. Obviously, that civilization is not yet ready for Alma Mater.

I thought of another university where in comparison the buildings are unpretentious and even inharmonious; whose formal entrances are only well-trodden pavements among the elms. Near the crest of the hill, instead of Alma Mater, stands a figure of Abraham Lincoln, extending no expressed welcome and, in his meditation, hardly conscious of the students or of the world about him. But from that statue of Lincoln there issues to youth more than a welcome, more than an invitation. From that homely figure there enters the soul of youth the story of great deeds, deeds brought to pass in spite of the bitterness of fellow countrymen and the abuse of a host of enemies. That statue typifies the university it adorns, for its beneficence endures notwithstanding the perversity of friends and foes.

When I was a boy I had the privilege of listening to a famous American orator deliver an oration on Lincoln that as yet has not been equalled. He said that here was a man against whom no harsher charge had ever been brought than this, that throughout his life he had been unable to do an unkind deed, and that of all the rulers of men who had exercised absolute power he alone had abused that power only to extend mercy.

I will not affront your intelligence by analyzing and interpreting the contrasting pictures of the two universities. They speak as in parables of deep and hidden things. Perhaps this university of ours is, after all, worthy of our devotion. Perhaps it may even be worthy of sacrifices from both of us. Perhaps this country of ours that protects and sustains such institutions may be worthy of our fidelity. Perhaps you and I are entitled to the joy that may come to us in defending our institution against those who would degrade it.

$\int$

I HAVE ATTEMPTED in this address to indicate, not by argument but merely by comment, that the Phi Beta Kappa approach to the good life is the best. The philosophical outlook on life and on human affairs can still keep us in the true course. The Heaven's Highway of the propagandist will end in the desert. The course for youth is not the billboarded concrete of the speedway. His course is less well marked but more inspiring. It leads over the wooded hills. There is steep climbing and some confusion. But there is much fragrance and much beauty and many inspiring vistas. There is joy on the road and room for many victories. It is a course planned and worked out by youth himself, with the aid of the rich material accumulated by many generations of wise pilots. But we need not climb forever. Nature has provided a parting of the roads where, after long effort, we are permitted to take the gentler slope. Age may finally part from youth. Not in gloom nor in sorrow, but in the glow of a new delight, we take the easy path, down, gently down, to the great sea. An Englishman has given me the words to say this. He is describing the junction where age parts from youth:

> *From here the road forks in twain;*
> *The one to darkling hills leads on;*
> *The one to distant seas.*
> *And all that I remember*
> *Is the evening growing late,*
> *And that from here the road forks in twain;*
> *For you, the one to wooded hills leads on,*
> *For me, to sunlit seas.*